Volume II

Biblical Hymns
and
Psalms

Volume II

Biblical Hymns
and
Psalms

by
Lucien Deiss, C.S.Sp.

Voice Edition

D-1929

WORLD LIBRARY PUBLICATIONS, Inc.

Accompaniment edition for organ and guitar
(D-3093— combination medium and low ranges)
available from publisher.

Printed in U. S. A.

The Text in Volume II was translated and adapted by Sister Kathleen Dougherty, S. S. M. N., and Lucien Deiss, C. S. Sp.

Some of the melodies in Volume II were inspired by the publications of Editions du Levain and are printed with their permission.

NIHIL OBSTAT
Rev. Giles H. Pater
Censor Deputatus
IMPRIMATUR
Most Rev. Paul F. Leibold
Archbishop of Cincinnati
January 25, 1970

Volume II — Deiss, Biblical Hymns and Psalms

Available in:
- Voice Edition (D-1929)
- Organ Accompaniment (D-3093 - combination medium and low ranges)
- Recordings:
    This Is the Day (FR-2002-SM)
    Songs in Celebration (FR-2001-SM)

Volume I — Deiss, Biblical Hymns and Psalms
Available in:
- Voice Edition (D-846-A)
- Organ Accompaniment (D-3092 - combination medium and low ranges)
- Unison Antiphons (D-1305-1)
- Brass Accompaniment for 7 psalms (D-1586)
- Recordings:
    Like Olive Branches (WLSM-21-S)
    With Joyful Lips (WLSM-23-S)

Volumes I and II of BIBLICAL HYMNS AND PSALMS have been published in the following editions:
Original edition — *French*
Translated editions — *English, Spanish, German, Italian, Chinese.*

CONTENTS

PUBLISHER'S NOTE

It might be well to note that there is one minor difference in the numbering system in the voice edition as compared with the accompaniment edition. Both utilize "a" and "b" — but to mean different things. The "a" or "b" after a hymn number in the voice edition, indicates that there are two different choir arrangements (SA, SATB, etc.) for that particular hymn. The "a" or "b" after a hymn number in the accompaniment edition, however, indicates that there are two settings of that hymn: one in medium range and one in low range.

FOREWORD

This volume is a continuation of my *Biblical Hymns and Psalms*. It is my wish that the music it contains, like that in Volume I, be a most obedient servant of the Word of God.

An appendix in the rear of the book ("Notes on the Hymns") contains copious notes indicating the precise sources and uses of the text of each hymn. There, too, are found commentaries on, and even, in some instances, prayers appropriate to certain hymns. These can be usefully employed especially in Bible Services.

For instance, the commentaries. To introduce a hymn by flatly stating "We will now sing song number . . . " is hardly the best method to give that hymn color and meaning. Rather the leader or commentator should compose his own commentary to introduce the song. In the event, however, that he lacks the necessary knowledge or time involved, I have supplied my own ready-made but, I hope, inspiring commentaries which can be used.

Likewise, the prayers. Whenever the commentator is unable to supply some original prayer of his own to be employed after the singing of the hymn itself, he is welcome to any in the appendix.

The congregation singing a hymn should not lack an awareness of the meaning of the hymn in the light of the Word of God. Especially is this true of hymns sung at the Communion Banquet itself. Therefore it is my recommendation that, after two or three verses of a hymn have been sung, the community pause to listen to the commentator read a relevant scripture passage before singing the remaining verses.

The appendix of this volume also supplies notes concerning the musical execution of the various hymns. These, together with the recordings of the various songs already available, will, I hope, afford sufficient knowledge for the faithful to render so creditable a musical performance of the hymns that they will be, I repeat, most obedient servants of the Word of God.

Lucien Deiss
Cincinnati
October 18, 1969

TOPICAL INDEX
for Volumes I and II
PART I
LITURGICAL YEAR

PART II
HYMNS AND PSALMS FOR THE MASS

Topical Index (cont.)

Topical Index (cont.)

PART III
HYMNS AND PSALMS FOR VARIOUS OCCASIONS

MORNING

EVENING

HOUSE OF THE LORD

WORD OF GOD

MISSIONS

BAPTISM

CONFIRMATION
See Pentecost

56. All Honor to You

ANTIPHON *for mixed voices*

All hon-or, pow-er to you, O Lord, now and ev-er-more!

VERSES *for mixed voices*

Repeat Antiphon

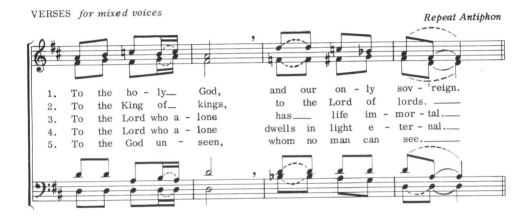

1. To the ho - ly___ God, and our on - ly sov - 'reign.
2. To the King of___ kings, to the Lord of lords. ___
3. To the Lord who a - lone has___ life im - mor - tal.___
4. To the Lord who a - lone dwells in light e - ter - nal.___
5. To the God un - seen, whom no man can see.___

ANTIPHON *for equal voices*

All hon-or, pow-er to you, O Lord, now and ev-er - more!

VERSES *for equal voices*

Repeat Antiphon

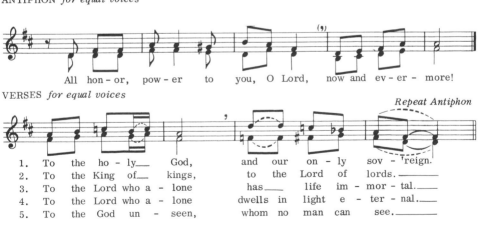

1. To the ho - ly___ God, and our on - ly sov - 'reign.
2. To the King of___ kings, to the Lord of lords.___
3. To the Lord who a - lone has___ life im - mor - tal.___
4. To the Lord who a - lone dwells in light e - ter - nal.___
5. To the God un - seen, whom no man can see.___

TEXT: **Doxology from 1 Timothy 6:15-16.**

USE: **Entrance. Recessional. Thanksgiving. Feast of Christ the King.**

57. Wisdom Has Built Herself a House

ANTIPHON I

Wis-dom has built her-self a house; she has pre-pared her ta-ble, has brought forth her wine; and she calls to her chil-dren.

ANTIPHON II *for mixed voices*

Come and eat of my bread, and drink of my wine; Come to the feast I pre-pared for you.

VERSES *for equal voices*

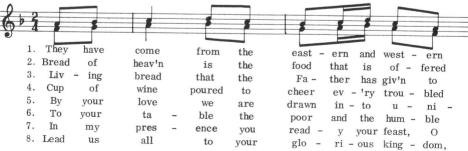

1. They have come from the east - ern and west - ern
2. Bread of heav'n is the food that is of - fered
3. Liv - ing bread that the Fa - ther has giv'n to
4. Cup of wine poured to cheer ev - 'ry trou - bled
5. By your love we are drawn in - to u - ni -
6. To your ta - ble the poor and the hum - ble
7. In my pres - ence you read - y your feast, O
8. Lead us all to your glo - ri - ous king - dom,

Wisdom Has Built Herself a House (cont.)

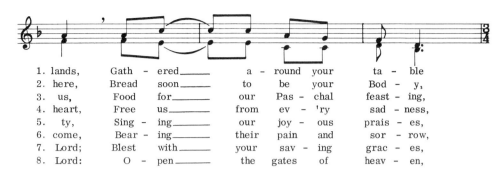

1.	lands,	Gath - ered___		a - round	your	ta -	ble
2.	here,	Bread soon___		to	be	your	Bod -	y,
3.	us,	Food for___		our	Pas -	chal	feast -	ing,
4.	heart,	Free us___		from	ev -	'ry	sad -	ness,
5.	ty,	Sing - ing___		our	joy -	ous	prais -	es,
6.	come,	Bear - ing___		their	pain	and	sor -	row,
7.	Lord;	Blest with___		your	sav -	ing	grac -	es,
8.	Lord:	O - pen___		the	gates	of	heav -	en,

Repeat Antiphon

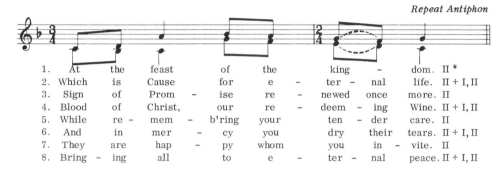

1.	At the feast	of	the	king -	dom.	II *
2.	Which is Cause	for	e -	ter - nal	life.	II + I, II
3.	Sign of Prom - ise	re -	newed	once	more.	II
4.	Blood of Christ,	our	re -	deem - ing	Wine.	II + I, II
5.	While re - mem - b'ring	your	ten -	der	care.	II
6.	And in mer - cy	you	dry	their	tears.	II + I, II
7.	They are hap - py	whom	you	in - vite.	II
8.	Bring - ing all	to	e -	ter - nal	peace.	II + I, II

ANTIPHON II *for equal voices*

I, II: Come___ and eat of my bread, and drink of my wine;

III: and drink of my wine;

Come to___ the feast___ I pre-pared for you.

Come to___ the feast I pre-pared for you.

* Roman numerals refer to Antiphon numbers.

TEXT: **Antiphon: Proverbs 9:1-5.**

USE: **Communion processional. Eucharist.**

58. All Blessed Are You, O Lord

mixed voices

ALLELUIA *Sing Alleluia first; then sing Verse I*

Al-le-lu – ia! Al-le-lu – ia! Al-le-lu – ia!

REFRAIN I

Glo – ry and praise to you in e – ter – ni – ty!

REFRAIN II

Repeat Alleluia

Glo – ry and praise to you in e – ter – ni – ty!

VERSES

Refrain I
1. All blessed are you, O Lord God of our fa – thers.

Refrain II + Alleluia
2. Blessed is your name of glo – ry, of ho – li – ness.

Refrain I
3. You are all blessed in the tem – ple of your ho – ly glo – ry.

Refrain II + Alleluia
4. You are all blessed on the throne of your king – dom.

All Blessed Are You, O Lord (cont.)

equal voices

ALLELUIA *Sing Alleluia first, then sing Verse I.*

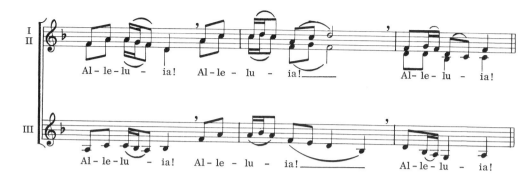

REFRAIN I

REFRAIN II *Repeat Alleluia each time Refrain II is sung.*

TEXT: **Canticle of the Three Children; Daniel 3:52-56.**

USE: **Hymn after Communion. Recessional. Thanksgiving.**

59a. You I Carry, O Lord

mixed voices

Capo 1: play E

ANTIPHON

You I car-ry, O Lord, in the cup of my hand, I a-dore you, my God, who rest up-on my lips. You whom the world could not hold in its li-mits, You whom heav-ens and earth pro-claim, joy-ous-ly sing-ing, You, my Lord, I re-ceive in my heart!

VERSES

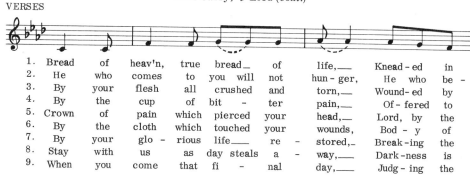

1. Bread of heav'n, true bread___ of life,___ Knead-ed in
2. He who comes to you will not hun-ger, He who be-
3. By your flesh all crushed and torn, Wound-ed by
4. By the cup of bit - ter pain,___ Of-fered to
5. Crown of pain which pierced your head, Lord, by the
6. By the cloth which touched your wounds, Bod - y of
7. By your glo - rious life___ re - stored,___ Break-ing the
8. Stay with us as day steals a - way,___ Dark-ness is
9. When you come that fi - nal day,___ Judg-ing the

1. love as food for our souls; We pray to you, O Lord:___
2. lieves in you will not thirst; We pray to you, O Lord:___
3. sin up - on___ the tree; We pray to you, O Lord:___
4. you on Cal - va - ry; We pray to you, O Lord:___
5. thorns that wound-ed your brow; We pray to you, O Lord:___
6. Christ, now si - lent in death; We pray to you, O Lord:___
7. bonds which held you in death; We pray to you, O Lord:___
8. hov - 'ring o - ver the earth; We pray to you, O Lord:___
9. world in mer - cy and love; We pray to you, O Lord:___

1. Bread which in mer - cy you give to us,
2. You are the bread of e - ter - nal life,
3. Your ho - ly death will be - come our peace,
4. Give us the grace___ to drink one day,
5. Place on our heads in that fi - nal hour,
6. Deep in the folds of your won - drous love,
7. Be to all na - tions the light of life,
8. Al - ways your pres - ence is near us, Lord,
9. Je - sus, re - mem - ber your faith - ful sons,

You I Carry, O Lord (cont.)

Repeat Antiphon

1. Par - don - ing, wip - ing a - way_____ our sins.
2. Bring - ing all men in - to un - i - ty.
3. And by your pain____ you bring_____ us joy.
4. Life - giv - ing wa - ter to set____ us free.
5. Crowns of sal - va - tion, e - ter - nal life.
6. Let all our faults be con - cealed____ from view.
7. Shine in your glo - ry, O ris - en Christ.
8. Glow - ing in splen - dor through - out____ our night.
9. Wel - come us in - to e - ter - nal life.

TEXT: Communion prayer in the Maronite Rite.

USE: Communion processional. Eucharist.

COMMENTARY: I bless you, Lord Jesus Christ, and give you thanks.
You whom the world could not hold in its limits,
You whom heavens and earth proclaim, joyously singing,
I receive in my heart!

PRAYER: God and Father of Jesus, your holy Son, our Savior,
cast your eyes upon us, upon your people here,
whom you have chosen through Christ,
to the glory of your name.

We give you thanks for having judged us worthy
to participate in your holy mysteries
and to have our dwelling near you.

Keep all priests blameless in your service,
keep the world in your almighty Providence,
pacify the nations who desire war,
sanctify the people, help the little children to grow,
strengthen those who seek the light.

Gather us all in your kingdom of heaven,
in Christ Jesus, our Lord,
forever and ever. Amen.

The Apostolic Constitutions (c. 380)

59b. You I Carry, O Lord

equal voices

Capo 1: play E

ANTIPHON

You I car-ry, O Lord, in the cup of my hand, I a-dore you, my

God, who rest up-on my lips. You whom the world could not hold in its

lim-its, You whom heav-ens and earth pro-claim joy-ous-ly sing-ing,

You, my Lord,_____ I re-ceive in my heart!_____

VERSES

1. Bread of heav'n, true bread_ of life,__ Knead-ed in
2. He who comes to you will not hun-ger, He who be-
3. By your flesh all crushed and torn,__ Wound-ed by
4. By the cup of bit - ter pain __ Of-fered to
5. Crown of pain which pierced your head,__ Lord, by the
6. By the cloth which touched your wounds, Bod-y of
7. By your glo-rious life__ re - stored, Break-ing the
8. Stay with us as day steals a - way,__ Dark-ness is
9. When you come that fi - nal day,__ Judg-ing the

1. love as food for our souls; We pray to you, O Lord:__
2. lieves in you will not thirst; We pray to you, O Lord:__
3. sin up - on__ the tree; We pray to you, O Lord:__
4. you on Cal - va - ry; We pray to you, O Lord:__
5. thorns that wound-ed your brow; We pray to you, O Lord:__
6. Christ, now si - lent in death; We pray to you, O Lord:__
7. bonds which held you in death; We pray to you, O Lord:__
8. hov - 'ring o - ver the earth; We pray to you, O Lord:__
9. world in mer - cy and love; We pray to you, O Lord:__

1. Bread which in mer - cy you give to us,
2. You are the bread of e - ter - nal life,
3. Your ho - ly death will be - come our peace,
4. Give us the grace__ to drink one day,
5. Place on our heads in that fi - nal hour,
6. Deep in the folds of your won - drous love,
7. Be to all na - tions the light of life,
8. Al - ways your pres - ence is near us, Lord,
9. Je - sus, re - mem - ber your faith - ful sons,

23

Repeat Antiphon

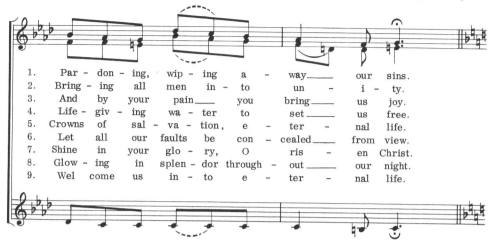

1. Par - don - ing, wip - ing a - way____ our sins.
2. Bring - ing all men in - to un - i - ty.
3. And by your pain____ you bring____ us joy.
4. Life - giv - ing wa - ter to set____ us free.
5. Crowns of sal - va - tion, e - ter - nal life.
6. Let all our faults be con - cealed____ from view.
7. Shine in your glo - ry, O ris - en Christ.
8. Glow - ing in splen - dor through - out____ our night.
9. Wel come us in - to e - ter - nal life.

When you go to Communion,
Place your cupped left hand
Under your right hand,
Making a throne to receive your king,
The Body of Christ,
*   And answer: Amen!*

After you have received the Body of Christ,
When you approach to drink of his blood,
Take the cup in both hands to drink,
And bow in an attitude of respect and adoration,
*   And say: Amen!*

St. Cyril of Jerusalem (313-386)
5th Catechesis of the Eucharist

60. Long Live the Lord

ANTIPHON *for mixed voices*

Long live the Lord,— for he is my sav-ior!

ANTIPHON *for equal voices*   *Congregation*

Long live the Lord,— for he is my sav-ior!

VERSES   *Congregation*
Cantor

1. For he is my light,
2. For he is my rock,
3. For he is my life,   for he is my sav-ior,
4. For he is my love,
5. For he is my way,

Cantor   *Congregation*

1. For he is my strong-hold,
2. For he is my ram-part,
3. For he is my re-fuge,   for he is my sav-ior,
4. In him joy for ev-er,
5. With him I am walk-ing,

Cantor

1.-5. For he is my Shep-herd, and to him I sing all my

Repeat Antiphon

prais-es, to him I pledge my love!

TEXT: Antiphon: Psalm 18:46.
USE: Acclamation to Christ. Entrance. Recessional.

61. The Spirit of God

ANTIPHON *for mixed voices*

The Spir-it of God rests up-on me,____ The Spir-it of God con-se-crates

me,____ The Spir-it of God bids me go forth to pro-claim his peace, his joy.

ANTIPHON *for equal voices*

The Spir-it of God rests up-on me,____ The Spir-it of God con-se-crates

me,____ The Spir-it of God bids me go forth to pro-claim his peace, his joy.

VERSES

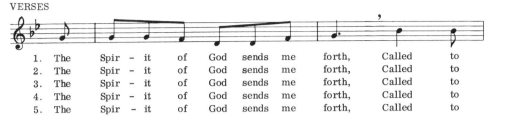

1. The Spir - it of God sends me forth, Called to
2. The Spir - it of God sends me forth, Called to
3. The Spir - it of God sends me forth, Called to
4. The Spir - it of God sends me forth, Called to
5. The Spir - it of God sends me forth, Called to

1. wit - ness the king - dom of Christ a - mong all the na - tions;
2. wit - ness the king - dom of Christ a - mong all the na - tions;
3. wit - ness the king - dom of Christ a - mong all the na - tions;
4. wit - ness the king - dom of Christ a - mong all the na - tions;
5. wit - ness the king - dom of Christ a - mong all the na - tions;

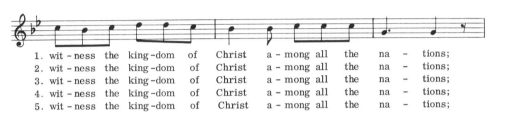

1. Called to pro - claim the good news of Christ to the poor.___ My
2. Called to con - sole the hearts o - ver - come with great sor - row. My
3. Called___ to com - fort the poor___ who mourn and who weep.___ My
4. Called to an - nounce the grace of sal - va - tion to men.___ My
5. Called to re - veal his glo - ry a - mong all the peo - ple. My

Repeat Antiphon

1. spir - it re - joic - es in God, my Sav - ior.
2. spir - it re - joic - es in God, my Sav - ior.
3. spir - it re - joic - es in God, my Sav - ior.
4. spir - it re - joic - es in God, my Sav - ior.
5. spir - it re - joic - es in God, my Sav - ior.

TEXT: **Isaiah 61:1-2; Luke 4:18-19.**

USE: **Pentecost. Priesthood. Missions.**

62a. On the Day

mixed voices

ANTIPHON

On the day when the ra - diant star of morn-ing shall rise in your heart, On the day when the glo-ry of the Lord will shine forth___ in splen-dor,

On the day when the Lord will wipe a - way all the tears from your eyes,

That day, face to face, you shall see God,___ our Fa - ther.

VERSES

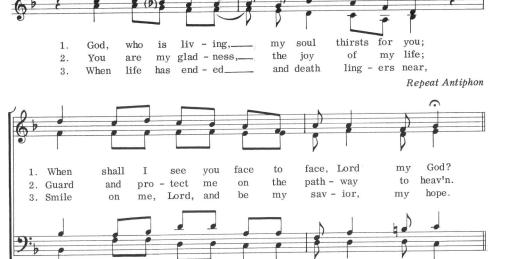

1,2,3. O Lord Je-sus, you are the first-born of the dead!

1. God, who is liv-ing,____ my soul thirsts for you;
2. You are my glad-ness,____ the joy of my life;
3. When life has end-ed____ and death ling-ers near,

Repeat Antiphon

1. When shall I see you face to face, Lord my God?
2. Guard and pro-tect me on the path-way to heav'n.
3. Smile on me, Lord, and be my sav-ior, my hope.

USE: **Advent. Funeral.**

COMMENTARY: **Let us sing of the day
on which the radiant star of morning
shall rise in our hearts.**

*On that day
the Lord will destroy the covering
that is cast over all peoples,
the veil that is spread over all nations.*

*He will swallow up death forever,
and the Lord will wipe away tears from all faces.*
Isaiah 25: 7-8

62b. On the Day

equal voices

ANTIPHON

On the day when the ra-diant star of mor-ning shall rise in your heart, On the day when the glo-ry of the Lord will shine forth in splen-dor, On the day when the Lord will wipe a - way all the tears from your eyes, That day, face to face, you shall see God our Fa - ther.

VERSES

1,2,3. O Lord Je - sus, you are the first-born of the dead!

1. God, who is liv - ing, my soul thirsts for you,
2. You, are my glad - ness, the joy of my life,
3. When life has end - ed and death lin - gers near,

Repeat Antiphon

1. When shall I see you face to face, Lord my God?
2. Guard and pro - tect me on the path - way to heav'n.
3. Smile on me, Lord, and be my sav - ior, my hope.

Praise the Lord with the sound of the trumpet,
praise him with lute and harp.
Praise him with timbrel and dance,
praise him with strings and pipes.
                    Psalm 150

63a. Without Seeing You

mixed voices

ANTIPHON

With - out see - ing you, we love you; with - out see - ing
you, we be - lieve; And we sing, Lord, in joy, your glo - ry.
You are our Sav - ior. We ____ be - lieve ____ in you.

VERSES

1. Blessed is he who will lis - ten to your Word; ____
2. He who lives in the Spir - it of the Word, ____
3. By our faith you a - bide with - in our hearts; ____
4. All my faith is in him who died for me, ____
5. By your grace you have saved us from our sins; ____
6. In our hearts may the fire of love still burn. ____
7. May we live in the bright-ness of your joy; ____
8. Re - u - nite all your peo - ple in one faith; ____

1. he	shall	tru - ly	nev - er	see	death,	for	by
2. he	shall	find his	true	life	in	you;	and	the
3. keep	us	safe - ly	with	you	in	love.	Give	to
4. for	it	is not	I	now	who	live;	it	is
5. in	our	hearts you	nour - ish	our	faith.	Our	sal -
6. Here	you	give your	Spir - it	to	men,	and	the
7. may	we	know the	peace	of	your	love;	may	we
8. lead	us	all to	heav - en - ly	joy.	We	will

1. you,	he	is	heir	to	a	new	life.
2. truth	of	your	word	makes	him	free,	Lord.
3. men	all	the	hope	of	your	pow'r,	Lord.
4. Christ	now	in	me,	my	sal - va -	tion.
5. va - tion	is	wrought	by	your	mer -	cy.
6. flame	of	that	fire	fills	the	whole	world.
7. sing	of	your	glo - ry	for - ev -	er.
8. see	your	face	for	all	a -	ges.

John 6: 68

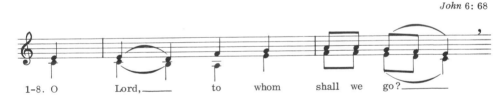

1-8. O Lord,____ to whom shall we go?____

Repeat Antiphon

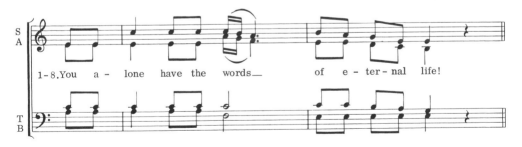

S
A

1-8. You a - lone have the words__ of e - ter - nal life!

T
B

TEXT: Antiphon adapted from 1 Peter 1:8
USE: Entrance. Communion processional. Feasts of Christ.
Celebrations of the Word of God.
COMMENTARY: Let us sing of Christ, our life and our joy:
Without seeing you, we love you,
and we sing, Lord, in joy, your glory!

63b. Without Seeing You

equal voices

ANTIPHON

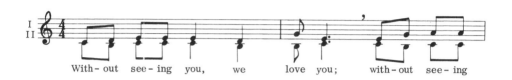

With- out see - ing you, we love you; with - out see - ing

you, we be - lieve; And we sing, Lord, in joy, your glo - ry.

You are our Sav - ior. We____ be - lieve__ in you.

VERSES

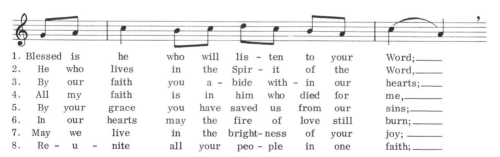

1.	Blessed	is	he	who	will	lis - ten	to	your	Word;____
2.	He	who	lives	in	the	Spir - it	of	the	Word,____
3.	By	our	faith	you	a -	bide	with - in	our	hearts;____
4.	All	my	faith	is	in	him	who	died	for	me,____
5.	By	your	grace	you	have	saved	us	from	our	sins;____
6.	In	our	hearts	may	the	fire	of	love	still	burn;____
7.	May	we	live	in	the	bright-ness	of	your	joy; ____
8.	Re -	u -	nite	all	your	peo - ple	in	one	faith;____

34

	1	2	3	4	5	6	7	8
1.	He	shall	tru - ly	nev - er	see death,	For	by
2.	He	shall	find his	true life	in you;	And	the
3.	Keep	us	safe - ly	with you	in love.	Give	to
4.	For	it	is not	I now	who live;	It	is
5.	In	our	hearts you	nour - ish	our faith.	Our	sal -
6.	Here	you	give your	Spir - it	to men,	And	the
7.	May	we	know the	peace of	your love;	May	we
8.	Lead	us	all to	heav - en - ly	joy.	We	will

1. you,   He   is   heir   to   a   new_____   life.
2. truth   of   your   word   makes   Him   free,____   Lord.
3. men   all   the   hope   of   your   pow'r,____   Lord.
4. Christ   now   in   me,   my   sal - va - tion.
5. va - tion   is   wrought   by   your   mer - cy.
6. flame   of   that   fire   fills   the   whole____   world.
7. sing   of   your   glo - ry   for - ev - er.
8. see   your____   face   for   all   a - ges.

John 6: 68

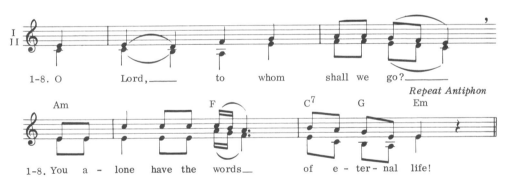

1-8. O   Lord,____   to   whom   shall   we   go?____

Repeat Antiphon

Am   F   C⁷   G   Em

1-8. You   a - lone   have   the   words__   of   e - ter - nal   life!

64. Jesus Christ, the Faithful Witness

ANTIPHON *for mixed voices*

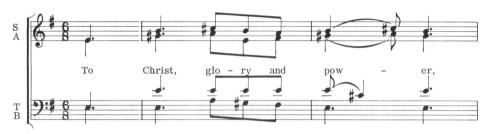

To Christ, glo - ry and pow - er,

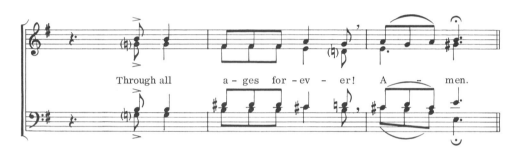

Through all a - ges for - ev - er! A - men.

ANTIPHON *for equal voices*

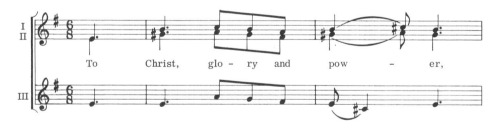

To Christ, glo - ry and pow - er,

Through all a - ges for - ev - er! A - men.

VERSES

Soloist

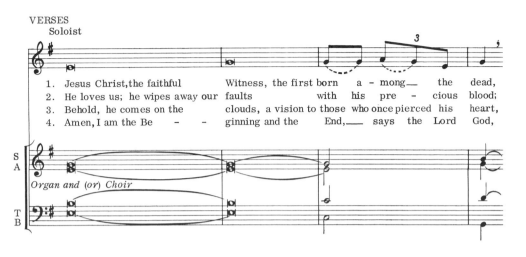

1. Jesus Christ, the faithful Witness, the first born a - mong___ the dead,
2. He loves us; he wipes away our faults with his pre - cious blood;
3. Behold, he comes on the clouds, a vision to those who once pierced his heart,
4. Amen, I am the Be - - ginning and the End,___ says the Lord God,

Organ and (or) Choir

(Repeat Antiphon)

1. Ruler and Lord of the kings___ of the earth.
2. He makes us a Kingdom of priests for God, his Fa - ther.
3. And all the nations shall mourn___ at the sight.
4. He who is, who was, and will come, the might - y one.

TEXT: **Revelation 1:5-7**

USE: **Entrance. Feasts of Christ. Advent** (see verse 3). **Easter** (see verse 1).

COMMENTARY: **Let us sing of Christ, the faithful Witness,
the first-born among the dead.
To him, glory and power,
through all ages forever!**

65. We Give You Thanks

ANTIPHON *for mixed voices*

We give you thanks,— we wor-ship you,— we

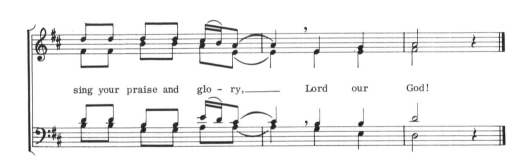

sing your praise and glo - ry,— Lord our God!

ANTIPHON *for equal voices*

We give you thanks,— we wor-ship you,— we

sing your praise and glo - ry,— Lord our God!

VERSES

S
A

1. To your peo - ple you give bread from heav - en,_____
2. You have giv - en us wine, bring - ing glad - ness,_____
3. To the king - dom of joy, peace, and hap - pi - ness,_____
4. To the Fa - ther, the Son, and the Spir - it,_____

unis.

S
A

1.___ the prom - ised bread of life.___ Those who will
2.___ the prom - ise of your love.___ Those who will
3.___ you lead your ho - ly peo - ple. Safe in the
4.___ we sing our hymns of praise;___ All hon - or,

T
B

Repeat Antiphon

1. eat of this bread, will not hun - ger___ a - gain.
2. drink from this cup, will not ev - er___ know thirst.
3. clasp of your hand, guard us ev - er___ in love.
4. glo - ry, and might, through all a - ges___ to come.

TEXT: The text of the Antiphon is used by the Eastern Liturgies, as
an acclamation of the people during the Eucharistic Prayer (Canon).

USE: Communion processional. Eucharist.

COMMENTARY: Receiving the bread of heaven,
we give you thanks, we worship you,
we sing your praise and glory,
Lord our God.

66. Blessed Be Our Lord

ANTIPHON

Al - le - lu - ia!___ Al - le - lu - ia!___
*Praise be to the Lord,___ Glo - ry to his name!

VERSES

Ps. 72: 18–19.

1. Bless - ed be our Lord, the God___ of Is - ra - el. *Antiphon*

2. For who a - lone works mar - vel - ous deeds for men? *Antiphon*

3. Bless - ed be his glo - rious name___ for - ev - er - more. *Antiphon*

4. Let all the earth be filled___ with his glo - ry. *Antiphon*

5. Praised be the Fa - ther, the Son, and Ho - ly Spir - it. *Antiphon*

6. Now and ev - er - more, through all the years to come. *Antiphon*

*The words "Praise be to the Lord, Glory to his name!" may be used during Lent.

ANTIPHON *for mixed voices*

ANTIPHON *for equal voices*

TEXT: **Psalm 72:18-19. Doxology ending the second book of the psalms.**

USE: **Recessional. Thanksgiving.**

COMMENTARY: **Alleluia! Blessed be the Lord, our God!**

67. Where Two or Three Are Gathered

ANTIPHON *for mixed voices*

"Where two or three are gath-ered in my name," says the Lord,

"There am I in the midst of them."___

ANTIPHON *for equal voices*

"Where two or three are gath-ered in my name," says the Lord,

"There am I in the midst of them."___

VERSES

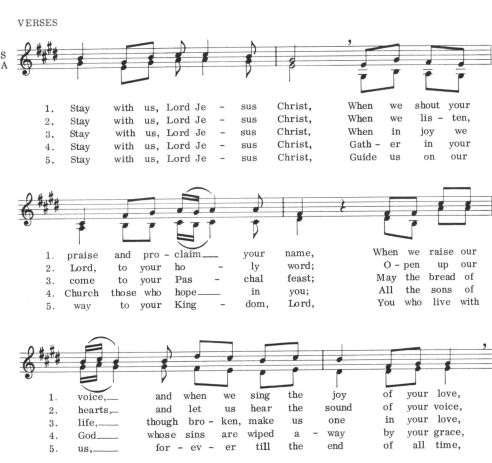

1.	Stay	with	us, Lord Je - sus	Christ,	When	we	shout	your
2.	Stay	with	us, Lord Je - sus	Christ,	When	we	lis -	ten,
3.	Stay	with	us, Lord Je - sus	Christ,	When	in	joy	we
4.	Stay	with	us, Lord Je - sus	Christ,	Gath -	er	in	your
5.	Stay	with	us, Lord Je - sus	Christ,	Guide	us	on	our

1.	praise	and	pro - claim___	your	name,	When we	raise our
2.	Lord,	to	your	ho - ly	word;	O - pen	up our
3.	come	to	your	Pas - chal	feast;	May the	bread of
4.	Church	those who	hope___	in	you;	All the	sons of
5.	way	to	your	King - dom,	Lord,	You who	live with

1.	voice,___	and when we	sing	the	joy	of	your	love,
2.	hearts,—	and let us	hear	the	sound	of	your	voice,
3.	life,___	though bro - ken,	make us	one	in	your	love,
4.	God___	whose sins	are wiped	a - way	by	your	grace,
5.	us,___	for - ev - er	till	the	end	of	all	time,

Repeat Antiphon

1.-5.	O	Lord, ___	our God,	Em - man - u - el!

TEXT: **Antiphon: Matthew 18:28.**

USE: **Entrance hymn for all celebrations.**

COMMENTARY: **Stay with us, Lord Jesus Christ!**
We are gathered in your name,
you are in the midst of your people.

68. This Is the Day

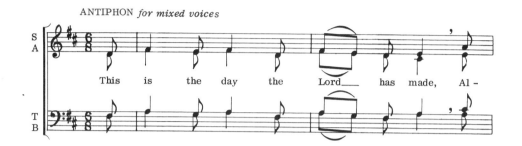

TEXT: Antiphon. Psalm 118:24.

USE: Easter and Easter time.

COMMENTARY: Let us sing of the day the Lord has made,
the day in which Christ is risen from the dead
and stays now with us, his living people,
Alleluia!

VERSES

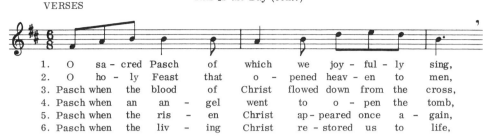

1. O   sa - cred Pasch   of   which   we   joy - ful - ly   sing,
2. O   ho - ly   Feast   that   o -   pened heav - en   to   men,
3. Pasch when   the blood   of   Christ flowed down from the   cross,
4. Pasch when   an   an - gel   went   to   o - pen   the   tomb,
5. Pasch when   the ris - en   Christ   ap - peared once   a - gain,
6. Pasch when   the liv - ing   Christ   re - stored us   to   life,

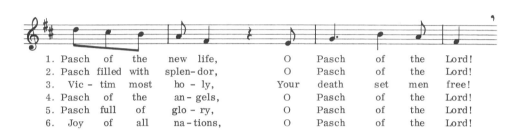

1. Pasch of   the   new life,   O   Pasch   of   the   Lord!
2. Pasch filled with splen-dor,   O   Pasch   of   the   Lord!
3. Vic - tim most ho - ly,   Your death set   men   free!
4. Pasch of   the   an - gels,   O   Pasch   of   the   Lord!
5. Pasch full of   glo - ry,   O   Pasch   of   the   Lord!
6. Joy   of   all   na - tions,   O   Pasch   of   the   Lord!

Repeat Antiphon

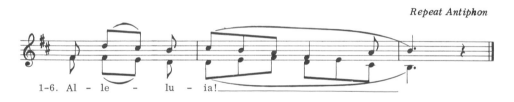

1-6. Al - le - lu - ia!

ANTIPHON *for equal voices*

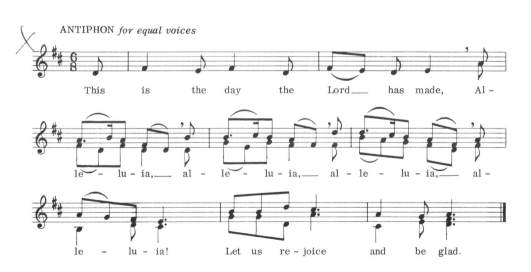

This   is   the   day   the   Lord___ has made,   Al -
le - lu - ia,___ al - le - lu - ia,___ al - le - lu - ia,___ al -
le - lu - ia!   Let us re - joice   and   be   glad.

69a. God Is Love

mixed voices

ANTIPHON

God is love;___ he who a-bides in love,___ a-bides in God; And God___ a-bides___ in him.

VERSES

1. Lord, your love u - nites us to - geth - er in one ac - cord.
2. Lord, be - hold your sons, now a - wait - ing your ten - der care.
3. Lord, your love is light, shin - ing bright-ly with - in the night.
4. Lord, your gift of love is the par - don for all our faults.
5. Lord, how great this love, which the Fa - ther has giv - en us.
6. Lord, my heart and soul sing their praise to the liv - ing God.

Repeat Antiphon

1. In this love, O Lord,___ may we___ know joy,___ on - ly joy in you.
2. Their eyes rest on you;___ lift your hands, Lord, o - pen wide our hearts.
3. Those who have no love___ will ev - er be___ liv-ing in the dark.
4. In your bod - y, Lord,___ and in___ your blood, we find life a-gain.
5. Love which tru - ly calls___ us Sons of God: this is what we are.
6. Call us to your home,___ u - nite___ us all, gath-er us as one.

69b. God Is Love

equal voices

ANTIPHON

God is love;— he who a - bides in love,—

a - bides in God; And God— a - bides— in him.

VERSES

1. Lord, your love u – nites us to - geth - er in one ac - cord;
2. Lord, be - hold your sons, now a - wait - ing your ten - der care;
3. Lord, your love is light, shin - ing bright -ly with - in the night;
4. Lord, your gift of love is the par - don for all our faults;
5. Lord, how great this love, which the Fa - ther has giv - en us;
6. Lord, my heart and soul sing their praise to the liv - ing God;

Repeat Antiphon

1. In this love, O Lord,— may we know joy, on - ly joy in you.
2. Their eyes rest on you;— lift your hands, Lord, o - pen wide our hearts.
3. Those who have no love— will ev - er be liv - ing in the dark.
4. In your bod - y, Lord,— and in your blood, we find life a - gain.
5. Love which tru - ly calls— us Sons of God: this is what we are.
6. Call us to your home,— u - nite us all, gath - er us as one.

TEXT: Antiphon: 1 John 4:16

USE: Entrance. Communion.

COMMENTARY: God is love. Let us sing of this love,
which gathers us together and calls us from death to life.

70a. Awake and Live

mixed voices

ANTIPHON

A - wake and live,___ O you who sleep, a - wake and rise___ from the dead. Let the light of Christ shine on you!

VERSES

1-8. Bap - tized in your death and raised to

1-8. life in your glo - ry, we sing to you, Je - sus Christ:

TEXT: Ephesians 5:14.

USE: Easter. Baptism. Entrance. Communion.

COMMENTARY: Let us sing to Jesus Christ, the risen Lord,
who awakes us from death
and calls us from darkness to light.

Awake and Live (cont.)

Repeat Antiphon

1. In you is the bright - ness which shines through -
2. The source of the wa - ter which takes a -
3. The sign of the Spir - it is set up -
4. You o - pen our lips___ and we praise your
5. Our souls are a - dorned___ for the splen - dor
6. You o - pen the door - way to par - a -
7. Your life - giv - ing word___ is now writ - ten
8. You dry all the tears___ which your chil - dren

(unis.)

1. out our night; And with this light, you il -
2. way our sins: O bread of heav'n, gift that
3. on our hearts, And on our souls the re -
4. ho - ly name. Teach us, O Lord, how to
5. yet to come; You are the way that will
6. dise a - gain; You bring us all to the
7. on our hearts; You are the prom - ise the
8. shed in pain: We sing your praise through all

(unis.)

1. lu - mine the whole___ world.
2. gives___ us a new___ life.
3. flec - tion of glo - ry.
4. pray to God the Fa - ther.
5. lead___ us to heav - ven.
6. feast___ of the king - dom.
7. Fa - ther has give - en.
8. a - ges, for - ev - er.

49

70b. Awake and Live

equal voices

ANTIPHON

A - wake and live, O you who sleep, a - wake and rise__ from the dead. Let the light of Christ shine on you!

VERSES

1-8. Bap - tized in your death and raised to life in your glo - ry, We sing to you, Je - sus Christ:

unis.

1. In you is the bright-ness which shines through-out our night; And
2. The source of the wa - ter which takes a - way our sins: O
3. The sign of the Spir - it is set up - on our hearts, And
4. You o - pen our lips__ and we praise your ho - ly name; Teach
5. Our souls are a - dorned for the splen-dor yet to come; You
6. You o - pen the door - way to par - a - dise a - gain; You
7. Your life - giv - ing word__ is now writ - ten on our hearts; You
8. You dry all the tears__ which your chil - dren shed in pain; We

Repeat Antiphon

1. with this light, you il - lu - mine the whole__ world.
2. Bread of heav'n, gift that gives us a new__ life.
3. on our souls the re - flec - tion of glo - ry.
4. us, O Lord, how to pray to God the Fa - ther.
5. are the way that will lead __ us to heav - en.
6. bring us all to the feast__ of the king - dom.
7. are the prom - ise the Fa - ther has giv - en.
8. sing your praise through all a - ges, for - ev - er.

71. Where Love and Charity Abide

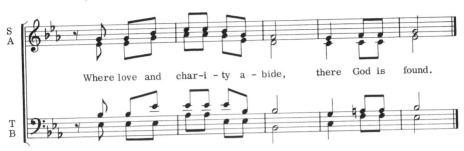

Where love and char-i-ty a-bide, there God is found.

ANTIPHON *for equal voices*

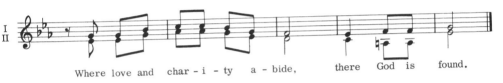

Where love and char-i-ty a-bide, there God is found.

VERSES

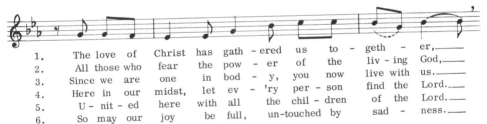

1. The love of Christ has gath-ered us to-geth-er,____
2. All those who fear the pow-er of the liv-ing God,____
3. Since we are one in bod-y, you now live with us.____
4. Here in our midst, let ev-'ry per-son find the Lord.____
5. U-nit-ed here with all the chil-dren of the Lord.____
6. So may our joy be full, un-touched by sad-ness.____

(Repeat Antiphon after each verse.)

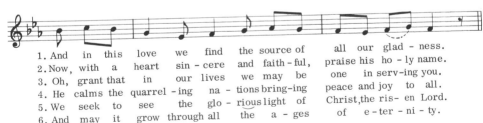

1. And in this love we find the source of all our glad-ness.
2. Now, with a heart sin-cere and faith-ful, praise his ho-ly name.
3. Oh, grant that in our lives we may be one in serv-ing you.
4. He calms the quarrel-ing na-tions bring-ing peace and joy to all.
5. We seek to see the glo-rious light of Christ, the ris-en Lord.
6. And may it grow through all the a-ges of e-ter-ni-ty.

TEXT: **Adaptation of** Ubi caritas et amor.
USE: **Entrance. Communion. Eucharist. Unity.**

72. You Alone Are Holy

ANTIPHON *for mixed voices*

You a-lone are ho-ly, you a-lone are Lord, you a-lone Je-sus Christ,
To the glo-ry of God the Fa - ther! A - men.

VERSES

1. For you are God's Son, born be-fore the world be-gan, You
2. For you are the pro - phet on whom the Spir-it rests, You
3. For you are the sun burst-ing forth up - on the dawn, You
4. In you is the good - ness, the ten-der love of God; You
5. For you are the path - way, the liv - ing road to God; You
6. For you are the prom - ise, the Fa-ther's gift to men; Your
7. For you, the Mes - si - ah, are hum - ble in your heart; You

1. show us the won-d'rous face of __ God. Sing to the Lord, praise him,
2. car - ry the joy of God to __ men. Sing to the Lord, praise him,
3. ban - ish the dark-ness of our __ sins. Sing to the Lord, praise him,
4. res - cue our souls from deep des - pair. Sing to the Lord, praise him,
5. o - pen the door to par a - dise. Sing to the Lord, praise him,
6. death brought the peace for which we __ long. Sing to the Lord, praise him,
7. com - fort the poor and rest - less __ souls. Sing to the Lord, praise him,

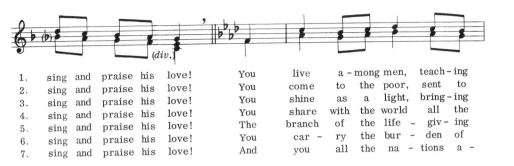

1.	sing and praise his love!	You	live	a - mong men,	teach-ing
2.	sing and praise his love!	You	come	to the poor,	sent to
3.	sing and praise his love!	You	shine	as a light,	bring-ing
4.	sing and praise his love!	You	share	with the world	all the
5.	sing and praise his love!	The	branch	of the life -	giv-ing
6.	sing and praise his love!	You	car - ry	the bur - den	of
7.	sing and praise his love!	And	you	all the na - tions	a -

1.	us to live as one; Now ga - ther us, Lord, in u - ni - ty.
2.	bring the Fa-ther's love, As blind men we lift our hands to__ you.
3.	bright-ness to the world; Come guide us to find the way to__ peace.
4.	peace and joy of God; You light - en the bur - dens of our hearts.
5.	vine, you lead the way while crush-ing the bonds of sin and death.
6.	sin for all the world, That we may have mer - cy, peace, and joy.
7.	wait with ea-ger hearts: Our Sav - ior, the hope of all man - kind.

Repeat Antiphon

Soloist: Sing to the Lord!

1-7. Sing to the Lord,__ praise him, sing and praise his love!_____

For antiphon for equal voices, see next page.

USE: **Feasts of Christ. Entrance. Communion.**

COMMENTARY: **In joy let us sing to our Lord:**
you alone are holy, you alone are Lord,
you alone are Jesus Christ.

53

ANTIPHON *for equal voices*

You a-lone are ho- ly, you a-lone are Lord, you a-lone Je-sus Christ,

To the glo-ry of God the Fa - ther! A - men.

73a. With Words of Praise
equal voices

ANTIPHON

Lord, fill my mouth with words of praise to you, and let my lips re-ech-o your joy when I sing, Lord, when I sing, Lord, when I sing, Lord, for you, my God, joy of my heart!

VERSES

1.-4. O my Lord!

1. O-pen our lips to praise you and bless your sav-ing pow'r.
2. You, the prom-ise of na-tions, the light of all man-kind.
3. Through your vic-t'ry you o-pen the door to last-ing life.
4. See the poor man, the hum-ble who beg now for your love.

1. Let our hearts be filled with hymns of praise and of joy.
2. The bright morn-ing star which shines its bright-ness in our hearts.
3. And your suf-f'rings show the path-way bring-ing us in to heav'n.
4. Give the bread of heav'n to save all na-tions from their sins.

Repeat Antiphon

1.-4. God of our love, God of our joy!

73b. With Words of Praise

mixed voices

ANTIPHON

Lord, fill my mouth with words of praise to you,

And let my lips re-ech-o your joy when I

sing, Lord, when I sing, Lord, when I sing, Lord, for you, my

VERSES

God, joy of my heart! 1.-4. O my Lord!

VERSES

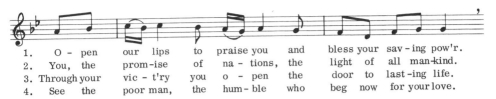

1. O - pen our lips to praise you and bless your sav - ing pow'r.
2. You, the prom-ise of na - tions, the light of all man-kind.
3. Through your vic - t'ry you o - pen the door to last -ing life.
4. See the poor man, the hum - ble who beg now for your love.

1. Let our hearts be filled with hymns of praise__ and of joy.
2. The bright morn - ing star which shines its bright-ness in our hearts.
3. And your suf-f'rings show the path - way bring-ing us in to heav'n.
4. Give the bread of heav'n to save all na - tions from their sins.

Repeat Antiphon

1. -4. God of our love,_____ God of our joy!

USE: **Hymn of praise. Entrance. Communion.**

57

74a. Lord, in Your Tenderness

mixed voices

ANTIPHON

Lord, in your ten-der-ness and mer-cy, you pre-pare a

feast for your peo-ple, for the poor man,___ who hun-gers still;

poor man who

and you o-pen the door-ways in-to your king-dom.

USE: Communion. Eucharist. Entrance. Unity.

COMMENTARY: Let us sing of the love of our Lord:
in his tenderness and mercy
he prepares for his people the table of his word,
as well as the table of his heavenly bread;
and he opens the doorways into his kingdom.

VERSES

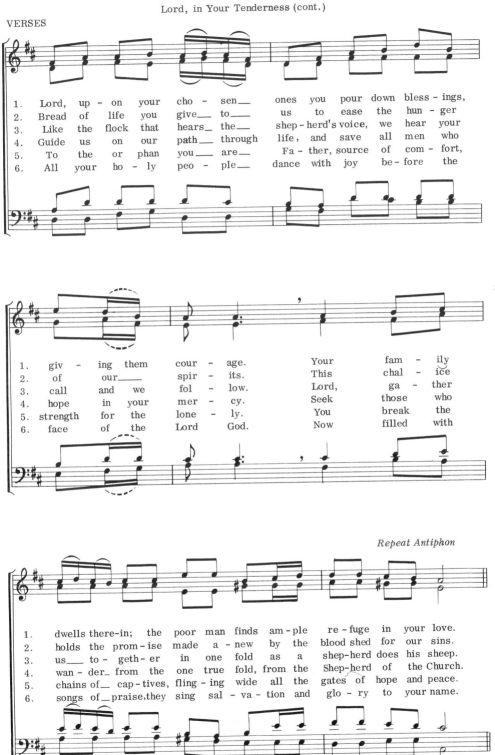

1. Lord, up - on your cho - sen___ ones you pour down bless - ings,
2. Bread of life you give___ to___ us to ease the hun - ger
3. Like the flock that hears_ the___ shep - herd's voice, we hear your
4. Guide us on our path_ through life, and save all men who
5. To the or phan you___ are___ Fa - ther, source of com - fort,
6. All your ho - ly peo - ple___ dance with joy be - fore the

1. giv - ing them cour - age. Your fam - ily
2. of our___ spir - its. This chal - ice
3. call and we fol - low. Lord, ga - ther
4. hope in your mer - cy. Seek those who
5. strength for the lone - ly. You break the
6. face of the Lord God. Now filled with

Repeat Antiphon

1. dwells there-in; the poor man finds am - ple re - fuge in your love.
2. holds the prom - ise made a - new by the blood shed for our sins.
3. us___ to - geth - er in one fold as a shep-herd does his sheep.
4. wan - der_ from the one true fold, from the Shep-herd of the Church.
5. chains of_ cap-tives, fling - ing wide all the gates of hope and peace.
6. songs of_praise,they sing sal - va - tion and glo - ry to your name.

59

74b. Lord, in Your Tenderness

equal voices

ANTIPHON

Congregation sings melody

Lord, in your ten-der-ness and mer-cy, you pre-pare a

feast for your peo-ple, for the poor man, who hun-gers still;

Congregation

And you o-pen the door-ways in - to your king-dom.

And you o-pen the door-ways in - to your king-dom.

VERSES

1. Lord, up - on your cho - sen ones you pour down bless - ings,
2. Bread of life you give to us to ease the hun - ger
3. Like the flock that hears the shep - herd's voice, we hear your
4. Guide us on our path through life, and save all men who
5. To the or - phan you are Fa - ther, source of com - fort,
6. All your ho - ly peo - ple dance with joy be - fore the

1. giv - ing them cour - age. Your fam - ily
2. of our spir - its. This chal - ice
3. call and we fol - low. Lord, ga - ther
4. hope in your mer - cy. Seek those who
5. strength for the lone - ly. You break the
6. face of the Lord God. Now filled with

Repeat Antiphon

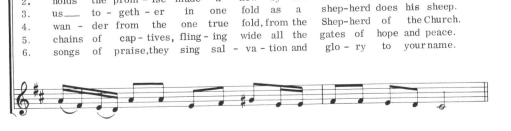

1. dwells there-in; the poor man finds am - ple re - fuge in your love.
2. holds the prom - ise made a - new by the blood shed for our sins.
3. us to - geth - er in one fold as a shep-herd does his sheep.
4. wan - der from the one true fold, from the Shep-herd of the Church.
5. chains of cap - tives, fling - ing wide all the gates of hope and peace.
6. songs of praise, they sing sal - va - tion and glo - ry to your name.

61

75. All Praise, Glory and Wisdom

ANTIPHON *for mixed voices*

All praise, glo-ry, and wis-dom, A - men!

Bless-ing and hon-or, pow-er and might, A - men!

To our God through all e-ter-ni-ty, A - men, A - men!

The small notes are sung by the congregation.

TEXT: Revelation 7:9-12.
USE: Entrance. Easter season. Thanksgiving. Feasts of All Saints.
COMMENTARY: With all the saints of heaven,
let us give praise, glory, and thanksgiving
to God our Father
and to his Son, the risen Lord.

VERSES

Soloist

Behold, there appears a great crowd which no man could num-ber,
Clothed in white robes, holding psalms in their hands,
And the angels before the throne, with the elders and the
four living crea-tures,

from all nations, from all peoples, from all tribes and tongues;
_____ they cry out with a might - y voice:
they kneel be - fore the throne, their fac - es to the ground.

They stand before the throne, and be - fore the Lamb.
"Salvation to our God who sits upon the throne, and___ to the Lamb."
They worship the Lord and___ sing this song.

Melody of the verses

Organ and (or) choir

ANTIPHON *for equal voices*

Choir   Congregation

All praise, glo - ry, and wis - dom, A - men!

Choir   Congregation

Bless - ing and hon - or, pow - er and might. A - men!

Choir   Congregation   *Slowly*

To our God through all e - ter-ni - ty, A - men, A - men!

*The small notes are sung by the congregation.

63

76. You, Lord, Are the Way

ANTIPHON *for mixed voices*

You, Lord, are the way; you are our life; you,— O Lord,— are the truth; you are our hope; you are our joy!

ANTIPHON *for equal voices*

You Lord, are the way; you are our life; you,— O Lord,— are the truth; you are our hope; you are our joy!

VERSES

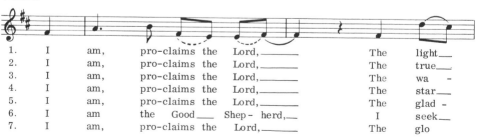

1.	I	am,	pro-claims the	Lord,____		The	light__
2.	I	am,	pro-claims the	Lord,____		The	true__
3.	I	am,	pro-claims the	Lord,____		The	wa -
4.	I	am,	pro-claims the	Lord,____		The	star__
5.	I	am,	pro-claims the	Lord,____		The	glad -
6.	I	am	the Good__	Shep - herd,__		I	seek__
7.	I	am,	pro-claims the	Lord,____		The	glo

1. which il-lu-mines the night.__ The man who
2. vine, and you are the branch-es. The man who
3. ter of life, source of joy.__ He who is
4. which pro-claims the new day.__ The sun-rise
5. ness which sings in your heart.__ On my re -
6. out and gath-er my sheep.__ If I should
7. ry which con-quers the grave.__ When you have

div.

1. fol-lows will walk in light for-ev - - er-more.
2. bears fruit will live in me and bring__ me joy.
3. thirst-ing will come to me and thirst__ no more.
4. burst-ing to bring to men e-ter - - nal dawn.
5. turn-ing, your trou-bled hearts will find__ their peace
6. call you, then lis-ten to my voice__ this day.
7. ris-en, I'll lead you to e-ter - - nal peace.

1-7. I live by my faith in the Son of God.__

Mixed voices　　　　　　　　　　　　　　　**Repeat Antiphon**

S
A

1-7. He loved__ me and gave him-self for me.

T
B

Equal voices　　　　　　　　　　　　　　　**Repeat Antiphon**

I
II

1-7. He loved__ me and gave him-self for me.

USE: **Feasts of Christ. Entrance. Communion.**
COMMENTARY: **We sing to you, Lord Jesus Christ:**
you are the way, the truth, and the life.

77a. Give the Bread of Life

mixed voices

ANTIPHON

Give the bread of life to us; give the cup that won us sal -

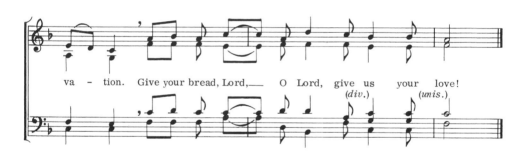

va - tion. Give your bread, Lord,___ O Lord, give us your love!
(div.) *(unis.)*

VERSES

1. God, my___ God, I___ seek you in the morn - ing;
2. I long to gaze on___ you with - in your dwell - ing,
3. All of my life I___ bless your ho - ly name;___
4. I look for you in the shad - ows of the eve - ning;
5. All through the day my___ soul clings fast to you;___

1. My soul is thirst - ing for you. Your praise is on my lips,__ O
2. See - ing your glo - ry and power. Your praise is on my lips,__ O
3. I lift my hands up to you. Your praise is on my lips,__ O
4. You are my thought in the night. Your praise is on my lips,__ O
5. Your hand sup - ports__ my life. Your praise is on my lips,__ O

1-5. Lord, and the joy of your love__ is in__ my heart.

1. My flesh is long - ing for you,
2. Your love is bet - ter than life;
3. My soul is fill - ed with your praise;
4. With - in the shad - ow of your wings,
5. All hon - or, glo - ry to the Father;

Repeat Antiphon

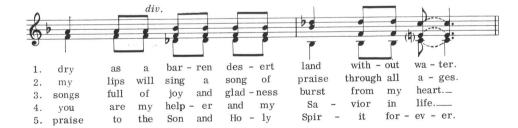

1. dry as a bar - ren des - ert land with - out wa - ter.
2. my lips will sing a song of praise through all a - ges.
3. songs full of joy and glad - ness burst from my heart.__
4. you are my help - er and my Sa - vior in life.__
5. praise to the Son and Ho - ly Spir - it for - ev - er.

67

77b. Give the Bread of Life

equal voices

ANTIPHON

Give the bread of life to us; give the cup that won us sal-

va - tion. Give your bread, Lord,— O Lord, give us your love!

VERSES

1. God, my— God, I— seek you in the morn-ing;
2. I long to gaze on— you with-in your dwell-ing,
3. All of my life I— bless your ho - ly name;—
4. I look for you in the shad - ows of the eve - ning;
5. All through the day my— soul clings fast to you;—

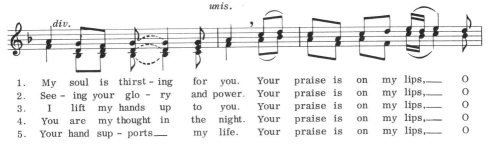

unis.

div.

1. My soul is thirst-ing for you. Your praise is on my lips,— O
2. See-ing your glo-ry and power. Your praise is on my lips,— O
3. I lift my hands up to you. Your praise is on my lips,— O
4. You are my thought in the night. Your praise is on my lips,— O
5. Your hand sup-ports— my life. Your praise is on my lips,— O

1-5. Lord, And the joy of your love— is in my heart.

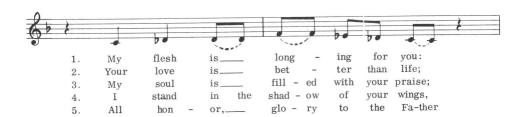

1. My flesh is— long - ing for you:
2. Your love is— bet - ter than life;
3. My soul is— fill - ed with your praise;
4. I stand in the shad - ow of your wings,
5. All hon - or,— glo - ry to the Fa-ther

Repeat Antiphon

div.

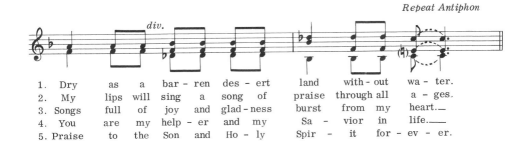

1. Dry as a bar - ren des - ert land with-out wa - ter.
2. My lips will sing a song of praise through all a - ges.
3. Songs full of joy and glad-ness burst from my heart.—
4. You are my help - er and my Sa - vior in life.—
5. Praise to the Son and Ho - ly Spir - it for - ev - er.

TEXT: **Verses adapted from Psalm 63(62).**

USE: **Communion. Eucharist.**

COMMENTARY: **"The cup which we bless,**
is it not a sharing of the blood of Christ?
And the bread which we break,
is it not a sharing of the body of Christ?
Because there is one bread,
we who are many are one body,
for we all partake of one bread." *I Corinthians 10:16-17*

Give this bread of life to us,
O Lord, give us your love!

78. Let Me Sing of Your Law

ANTIPHON *for mixed voices*

Let me sing of your law, O my God;
let your love come up - on your peo - ple.

VERSES

1. Through your own word,___ Lord, give us life;
2. I have made known___ to you my ways;
3. Show me the way___ to keep your law;
4. Deep in my soul___ my sor - row lies;
5. O take me far___ from e - vil ways,
6. With - in your law___ I choose to live;
7. My heart is strong,___ my joy is full;
8. Praise to the Fa - ther and to the Son;

Repeat Antiphon

1. In your ho - ly keep - ing, hap - py is my soul.
2. You have heard my plead - ing; now teach me your laws.
3. Let your ho - ly pre - cepts dwell with - in my mind.
4. Ev - er keep your prom - ise, let my heart be glad.
5. And in your great mer - cy, guide me in your paths.
6. In the paths of wis - dom I walk ev - er - more.
7. Fol - low - ing your law, Lord, free - ly do I walk.
8. Glo - ry to the Spir - it now and ev - er - more.

ANTIPHON *for equal voices*

Congregation

Let me sing of your law, O my God,——

Let me sing of your law, O my God,——

Congregation

Let your love—— come up - on your peo - ple.

Let your love—— come up - on your peo - ple.

TEXT: Adapted from Psalm 119:25-32.

USE: Entrance. Celebration of the Word of God.

COMMENTARY: Let me sing of your law, O my God;
let your love come upon your people.

71

79. Salvation, Glory, and Power

ANTIPHON   *mixed voices*

Al - le-lu - ia, Sal - va - tion, glo-ry and pow-er be to our God! Al - le-lu - ia, He reigns through all the a-ges to come!

VERSES

S: Al-le-lu - ia, _____ al - le-lu-
A: Al - le-lu - ia,

S: ia, _____ al-le-lu - ia, _____ al -
A: al - le-lu-ia, _____ al-le-lu-ia, _____

T:
1. Al - le-lu - ia! He has built his king -
2. Shout for joy, be filled with songs of
3. Now be - hold the mar - riage of the
4. She is robed in lin - en, bright and
5. Hap - py those in - vi - ted to the

B: Al - le-lu - ia, _____ al-le-lu-ia,

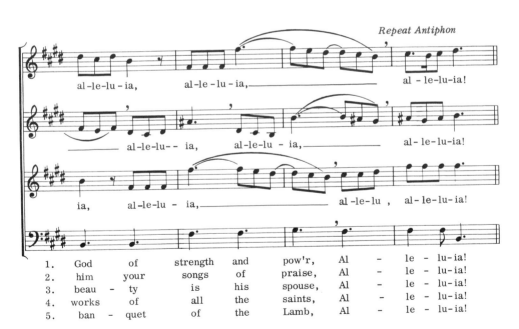

TEXT: Hymn of the elect in heaven, Revelation 16:6-9.

USE: Easter and all feasts of Christ. Feast of All Saints. Communion hymn.

80.   Joy to You

ANTIPHON *for mixed voices*

Joy to you, O Vir-gin Mar-y, Moth-er of the Lord!

ANTIPHON *for equal voices*

Joy to you, O Vir-gin Mar-y, Moth-er of the Lord!

VERSES

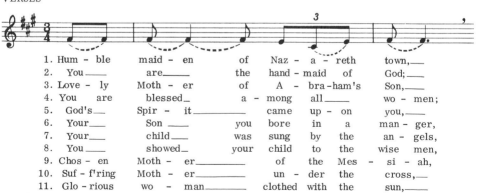

1. Hum - ble   maid - en   of   Naz - a - reth   town,___
2. You___   are___   the   hand - maid   of   God;___
3. Love - ly   Moth - er   of   A - bra-ham's   Son,___
4. You   are   blessed___   a - mong   all___   wo - men;
5. God's___   Spir - it___   came   up - on   you,___
6. Your___   Son___   you   bore   in   a   man - ger,
7. Your___   child___   was   sung   by   the   an - gels,
8. You___   showed___   your   child   to   the   wise   men,
9. Chos - en   Moth - er___   of   the   Mes - si - ah,
10. Suf - f'ring   Moth - er___   un - der   the   cross,___
11. Glo - rious   wo - man___   clothed   with   the   sun,___

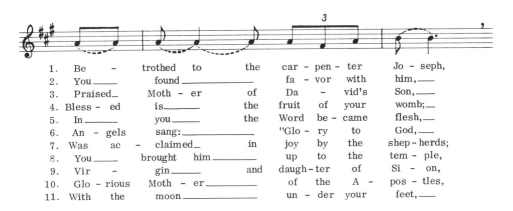

1. Be - trothed to the car - pen - ter Jo - seph,
2. You____ found____ fa - vor with him,____
3. Praised_ Moth - er of Da - vid's Son,____
4. Bless - ed is____ the fruit of your womb;____
5. In____ you____ the Word be - came flesh,____
6. An - gels sang:____ "Glo - ry to God,____
7. Was ac - claimed_ in joy by the shep - herds;
8. You____ brought him____ up to the tem - ple,
9. Vir - gin____ and daugh-ter of Si - on,
10. Glo - rious Moth - er____ of the A - pos - tles,
11. With the moon____ un - der your feet,____

Repeat Antiphon

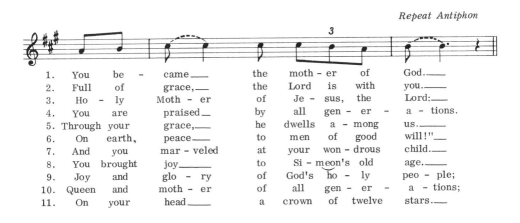

1. You be - came____ the moth - er of God.____
2. Full of grace,____ the Lord is with you.
3. Ho - ly Moth - er of Je - sus, the Lord:____
4. You are praised by all gen - er - a - tions.
5. Through your grace,____ he dwells a - mong us.____
6. On earth, peace____ to men of good will!"____
7. And you mar - veled at your won - drous child.____
8. You brought joy____ to Si - meon's old age.____
9. Joy and glo - ry of God's ho - ly peo - ple;
10. Queen and moth - er of all gen - er - a - tions;
11. On your head____ a crown of twelve stars.____

Melody of the verses

Organ and (or) choir

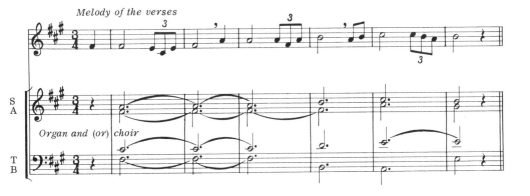

81a. Within Your Splendor

mixed voices

ANTIPHON I

With-in your splen-dor and in your beau-ty, you reign tri-um-phant,__ O Vir-gin Mar - y!

ANTIPHON II

You are all beau-ti-ful, O Vir-gin Mar - y, you are all beau-ti-ful!

VERSES

1. O lis - ten, my daugh - ter, lis - ten, and hear my
2. For he is the Lord; all hon - or and praise are
3. In gar - ments of wealth, a - dorned as a queen she
4. And fol - low - ing af - ter, mai - dens a - wait her
5. Your name will be blest through - out all the days to
6. My heart o - ver - flows with joy as I sing your
7. All hon - or and praise and bless - ings to Mar - y's
8. O Moth - er of God and Moth - er of all man -

Repeat Antiphon

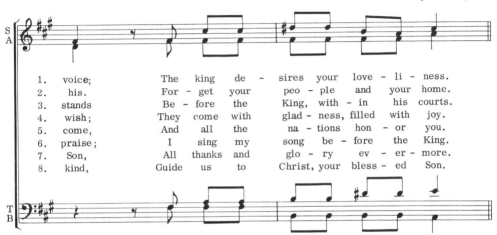

1. voice; The king de - sires your love - li - ness.
2. his. For - get your peo - ple and your home.
3. stands Be - fore the King, with - in his courts.
4. wish; They come with glad - ness, filled with joy.
5. come, And all the na - tions hon - or you.
6. praise; I sing my song be - fore the King.
7. Son, All thanks and glo - ry ev - er - more.
8. kind, Guide us to Christ, your bless - ed Son.

TEXT: Isometric adaption of Psalm 45(44).

USE: Feasts of Our Lady.

COMMENTARY: Let us sing of the Virgin Mary:
in her splendor and her beauty
she reigns triumphant near her Son, the Lord.

PRAYER: God our Father,
we give you thanks and bless you,
that you have chosen the Virgin Mary
to become the mother of your Son.

In her, your Word found a servant;
your love made her a Queen.

We beg you: May we follow her example
of listening to your Word
and acting upon it.

May we partake in the eternal joy
which you give us in Christ, your Son,
our Savior and our Brother,
forever and ever. Amen.

81b. Within Your Splendor

equal voices

ANTIPHON I

With - in your splen - dor and in your beau - ty, you reign tri - um - phant, __ O Vir - gin Mar - y!

ANTIPHON II

You are all beau - ti - ful, O Vir - gin Mar - y, you are all beau - ti - ful!

VERSES

1. O lis - ten, my daugh - ter, lis - ten, and hear my
2. For he is the Lord; all hon - or and praise are
3. In gar - ments of wealth, a - dorned as a queen she
4. And fol - low - ing af - ter, mai - dens a - wait her
5. Your name will be blest through - out all the days to
6. My heart o - ver - flows with joy as I sing your
7. All hon - or and praise and bless - ings to Mar - y's
8. O Moth - er of God and Moth - er of all man -

Repeat Antiphon

div.

1. voice; The king de - sires your love - li - ness.
2. his. For - get your peo - ple and your home.
3. stands Be - fore the King, with - in his courts.
4. wish; They come with glad - ness, filled with joy.
5. come, And all the na - tions hon - or you.
6. praise; I sing my song be - fore the King.
7. Son, All thanks and glo - ry ev - er - more.
8. kind, Guide us to Christ, your bless - ed Son.

82. Lord, Have Mercy

2-FOLD INVOCATIONS

for mixed voices

S. A.

Lord, have mer - cy. Lord, have mer - cy. Christ, have mer - cy.

T. B.

Christ, have mer - cy. Lord, have mer - cy. Lord, have mer - cy.

for equal voices

Lord, have mer - cy. Lord, have mer - cy.

Christ, have mer - cy. Christ, have mer - cy.

Lord, have mer - cy. Lord, have mer - cy.

83a. Lord, Have Mercy

3-FOLD INVOCATIONS

for mixed voices

83b. Lord, Have Mercy

3-FOLD INVOCATIONS

for equal voices

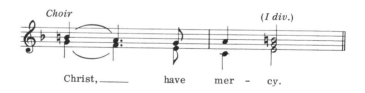

84a. Glory to God in the Highest

*for mixed voices
and congregation*

God, Lamb of God, you take a-way the sin of the world: have mer-cy on us; you are seat-ed at the right hand of the Fa-ther:___ re - ceive our___ prayer. For you a - lone are the Ho - ly One, you a - lone are the Lord, you a - lone are the Most High, Je - sus Christ, with the Ho - ly Spir- it, in the glo - ry___ of God the Fa - ther. A - men.

84b. Glory to God in the Highest

*for equal voices
and congregation*

85. Liturgy of the Word

ACCLAMATIONS

For the first and second reading

Lector or Cantor — This is the Word of the Lord. *Congregation* — Thanks be to God.

for mixed voices — Thanks be to God.

for equal voices — Thanks be to God.

For the Gospel

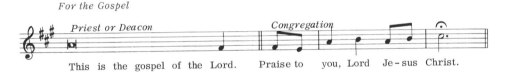

Priest or Deacon — This is the gospel of the Lord. *Congregation* — Praise to you, Lord Je-sus Christ.

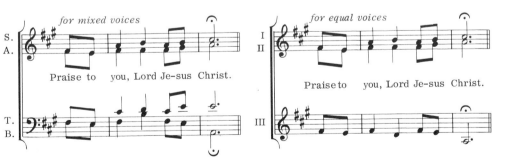

for mixed voices — Praise to you, Lord Je-sus Christ.

for equal voices — Praise to you, Lord Je-sus Christ.

86. Your Words, O Lord

Use: *Alleluia before the Gospel*

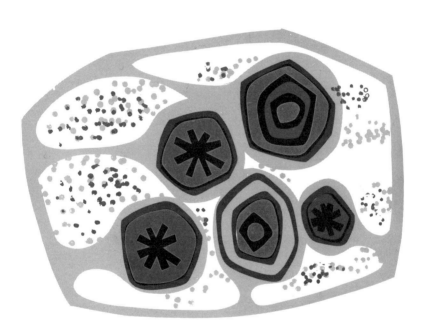

87. General Intercessions

RESPONSES
for mixed voices

1. O Lord, have mer - cy.
2. We pray to you, O Lord.
3. Re - mem - ber us, O Lord.
4. Ky - ri - e e - le - i - son.
5. Re - mem - ber us, O Lord, in your king - dom.
6. O Lord, hear us, we pray; O Lord, give us your love!

4 *voices.* **Congregation sings voice II**

7 O Lord, give us your love.

8 O Lord, give us your love.

Advent

9 Em - man - u - el! Come, save your peo - ple.

10 Come, Je - sus Christ, come, save your peo - ple.

Christmas

11 Glo - ry to God on high!

O   Lord,   give us your love.   O   Lord,   give   us   your   love.

Advent

Em - man - u - el!   Come,   save   your   peo - ple.

Come,   Je - sus Christ,   come,   save   your   peo - ple.

Christmas

Glo - ry   to   God   on   high!

Lent

12 Have mer - cy, O Lord, have mer - cy on us.

Easter Season

13 Christ, who is ris - en from the dead, have mer - cy on us.

Pentecost

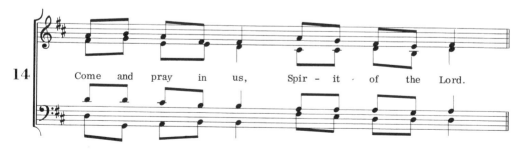

14 Come and pray in us, Spir - it of the Lord.

Lent

Have mer - cy, O Lord, have mer - cy on us.

Easter Season

Christ, who is ris - en from the dead, have mer - cy on us.

Pentecost

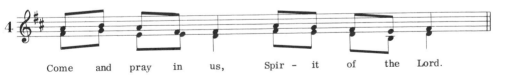

Come and pray in us, Spir - it of the Lord.

88. If You Bring Your Gift

INTRODUCTION

If you bring your gift to the al - tar,

and there you re - mem - ber that your broth - er has

(*to Antiphon*)

some-thing a - gainst you, leave your gift at the al - tar.

ANTIPHON *for mixed voices*

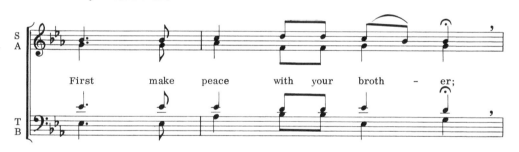

First make peace with your broth - er;

then come, of - fer your gift at the al - tar.

If You Bring Your Gift (cont.)

VERSES

1. It is love that I wish, and not an emp - ty
2. Let the man who has bread now share with those who

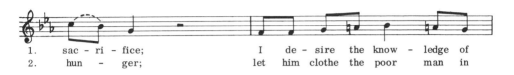

1. sac - ri - fice; I de - sire the know - ledge of
2. hun - ger; let him clothe the poor man in

Repeat Antiphon First make peace *after each verse.*

1. God, and not a worth - less of - f'ring.
2. need, in love and ten - der mer - cy.

After the second verse may be sung: Antiphon, introduction, Antiphon.

ANTIPHON *for equal voices*

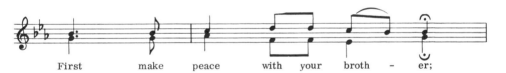

First make peace with your broth - er;

Then come, of - fer your gift at the al - tar.

TEXT: Antiphon: Matthew 5:23-24.
Verse 1: Hosea 6:6; Matthew 9:13.
Verse 2: Isaiah 58:7.

USE: Offertory processional, while the gifts are brought to the altar.

89. With a Joyful Heart

ANTIPHON
for mixed voices

With a joy - ful heart, O Lord,— my God, I give all to you.

ANTIPHON
for equal voices

With a joy - ful heart, O Lord,— my God, I give all to you.

VERSES

1. Be - hold, O Lord, this bread Which we now car - ry to your
2. Be - hold, O Lord, this wine; ac - cept and bless it for our
3. We come to you, O Lord; we bring the gifts that you have

(Repeat Antiphon)

1. al - tar. This bread will be - come your Bo - dy.
2. glad - ness. This wine will be - come your Blood.—
3. made,— the gifts we re - turn to you.—

TEXT: **Antiphon and Verse 3: 1 Chronicles 29:14, 17.**

USE: **Offertory processional, while the gifts are brought to the altar.**

90. Holy, Holy, Holy

for mixed voices

Ho-san-na,— ho-san-na,— ho-san-na— in— the high-est.

for equal voices

Ho - san - na,— ho - san - na,— ho-san - na— in the high-est.

(Repeat Hosanna optional)

Ho - ly, ho - ly, ho - ly Lord,— God of power and might.

(Repeat Hosanna)

Heav - en and earth are full— of— your glo — — ry.

(Repeat Hosanna)

Bless-ed is he who comes— in the name of the Lord.—

This hymn may be sung in the traditional manner by starting with the Holy, holy, holy and omitting the Hosanna after might. If it is desired to emphasize the acclamation character of this hymn, use the Hosanna as an antiphon, singing it at the beginning and repeating it after each phrase as indicated.

91.   Acclamations

for mixed voices

We give you thanks and glo-ry, Al-le-lu - ia,____

For your love is ____ with-out end, Al-le-lu - ia.

for equal voices

We give you thanks and glo-ry, Al-le-lu - ia.____

For your love is ____ with-out end, Al-le-lu - ia. ____

(div.)

for mixed voices

We give you thanks,—— we wor-ship you,—— we
sing your praise and glo-ry,—— Lord our God.

for equal voices

We give you thanks,—— we wor-ship you,—— we
sing your praise and glo-ry,—— Lord our God.

92. Christ Has Died

Let us proclaim the mystery of faith:

for mixed voices

Christ has died, Christ is ris-en, Christ will come a-gain.

for equal voices

Christ has died, Christ is ris-en, Christ will come a-gain.

93. Great Amen

I

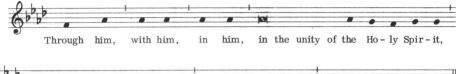

Through him, with him, in him, in the unity of the Ho - ly Spir - it,

all glory and hon-or is yours, al - might - y Fa-ther, for ev - er and ev - er.

Through him,
with him,
in him,
in the unity of the Holy Spirit,
all glory and honor is yours,
almighty Father,

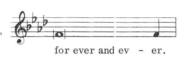

for ever and ev - er.

Mixed voices

A - men, a - men, a - men!

Equal voices

A - men, a - men, a - men!

II

Through him,
with him,
in him,
in the unity of the Holy Spirit,
all glory and honor is yours,
almighty Father,

for ever and ev - er.

Mixed voices

A - men, a - men, a - men!

Equal voices

A - men, a - men, a - men!

III

Through him,
with him,
in him,
in the unity of the Holy Spirit,
all glory and honor is yours,
almighty Father,

for ever and ev - er.

Mixed voices

A - men, a - men, a - - men!

Equal voices

A - men, a - men, a - - men!

94a. Our Father

INTRODUCTION

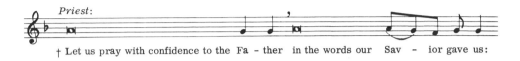

† Let us pray with confidence to the Fa - ther in the words our Sav - ior gave us:

ALTERNATE INTRODUCTION*

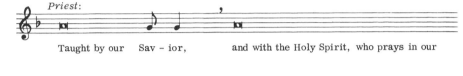

Taught by our Sav - ior, and with the Holy Spirit, who prays in our

hearts, crying: "Ab - ba, Fa - ther," in joy we say:

OUR FATHER
for mixed voices
Recitative

S A

Our Fa - ther, who art in heav - en, hal - lowed be thy name;

T B

thy king-dom come, thy will be done on earth as it is in heav-en.

Give us this day our dai - ly bread; and for-give us our tres-pass-es

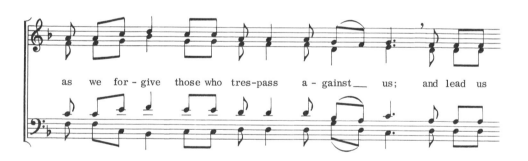

as we for - give those who tres-pass a - gainst___ us; and lead us

Prayer concludes on p. 108.

not in - to temp- ta - tion, but de - liv - er us from e - vil.

94b. Our Father

for equal voices
Recitative

Our Fa-ther, who art in heav-en, hal-lowed be thy name; thy king-dom come, thy will be done on earth as it is in heav-en. Give us this day our dai-ly bread; and for-give us our tres-pass-es as we for-give those who tres-pass a-gainst__ us; and lead us

Prayer concludes on next page.

not in-to temp-ta-tion, but de-liv-er us from e-vil.

Our Father (cont.)

EMBOLISM

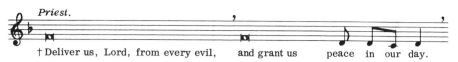

† Deliver us, Lord, from every evil,   and grant us   peace   in   our   day.

In   your   mercy   keep   us   free from sin   and protect us from all anxiety

as   we   wait in joyful hope   for   the   coming   of   our   Sav-ior Je-sus Christ.

DOXOLOGY
for mixed voices
   People:

†For the   king-dom, the pow-er and the   glo-ry are yours,   now and for ev - er.

for equal voices
   People:

†For the   king-dom, the pow-er and the   glo-ry are yours,   now and for ev - er.

† See footnote on p. 105.

95. Lamb of God
SIMPLE FORM

for mixed voices

Lamb of God, you take a - way the sins of the world,

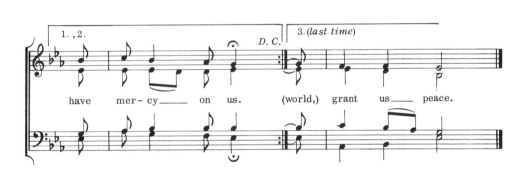

have mer - cy____ on us. (world,) grant us____ peace.

for equal voices

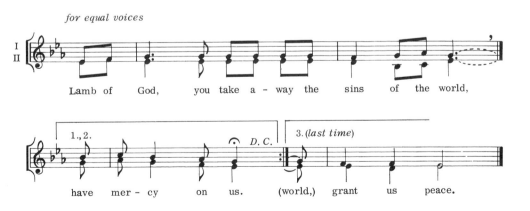

Lamb of God, you take a - way the sins of the world,

have mer - cy on us. (world,) grant us peace.

96a. Lamb of God

mixed voices

Lamb of God, ___ you take a-way the sins ___ of the

Lamb of God, Lamb of God, Lamb of God, Lamb of God,

world, have mer - cy on us, have mer - cy on us.

Lamb of God, Lamb of God, ___ Lamb of God, have mer - cy on us.

Lamb of God, ___ you take a - way the sins ___ of the

Lamb of God, Lamb of God, Lamb of God, Lamb of God,

world, have mer - cy on us, have mer - cy on us.

Lamb of God, Lamb of God, ___ Lamb of God, have mer - cy on us.

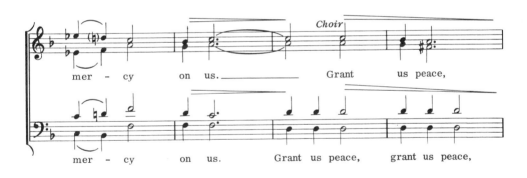

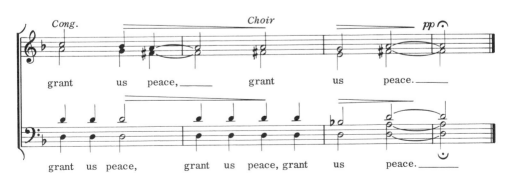

96b. Lamb of God

equal voices

97. In the Peace of Christ

Capo 1: play E

ANTIPHON *for mixed voices*

In the peace of Christ, we sing our thanks to God.

ANTIPHON *for three equal voices*

In the peace of Christ, we sing our thanks to God.

opt.
div.

VERSES

1. We give you thanks, O Lord. You have giv - en us your
2. We give you thanks, O Lord. You have giv - en us your
3. We give you thanks, O Lord. You have giv - en us a

Repeat Antiphon

1. sa - cred word to light our path to heav - en.
2. bread that is our pledge___ of e - ter - nal life.
3. song to praise your name___ through - out all the earth.

USE: **Recessional. Thanksgiving.**

NOTES ON THE HYMNS

(Appendix)

56. ALL HONOR TO YOU
Text:

This doxology, which we find in *1 Tim. 6:15-16,* was used in liturgical celebrations in the synagogues as well as in early Christian communities. It proclaims the eternal sovereignty of the Lord in opposition to the pagan practice of worshipping idols and even emperors.

Musical Performance:

Tempo, Largo; solemnly. ♩ = 80.

57. WISDOM HAS BUILT HERSELF A HOUSE
Text:

Antiphon: *Prov. 9:1-5.*
Verse 1: *Mt. 8:11* and *Lk. 13:29.*
Verse 2: *Jn. 6:32-33, 58.*
Verse 3: This is my body which shall be given up for you; do this in memory of me . . . This cup is the new covenant in my blood; do this as often as you drink it in memory of me. *I Cor. 11:24-25.*
Verse 5: There is one bread; we though many, are one body, as we partake of this one bread. *I Cor. 10:17.*
Verse 6: The Master of the house said to his servants, "Go out quickly into the streets and lanes of the city, and bring in here the poor, and the crippled, and the blind, and the lame, so that my house may be filled." *Lk. 14:23.*

Commentary:

Wisdom has built herself a house —
the Church of the Lord Jesus Christ.
She has prepared the table of the Eucharist;
she has mixed the wine of the divinity of Christ
with the water of human frailty,
and she calls to us all,
"Come and eat of my bread,
and drink of my wine;
come to the feast I prepared for you."

Musical Performance:

After verses 2, 4, 6, and 8, be certain to sing the antiphons exactly as indicated. Variety can be obtained in the verses by having verse 1 sung by sopranos and altos, verse 2 by tenors and basses, etc. Keep the rhythm steady; in this hymn the rhythm has the same importance as the melody. ♩ = 80.

58. ALL BLESSED ARE YOU, O LORD
Musical Performance:

Tempo, moderato. ♩ = 72. Maintain the rhythm strictly in both the antiphon and the verses, and also in connecting the verses and the antiphon. This hymn is written in such a style that the text of the antiphon is an answer to the text of the verses. Therefore the verses should be sung by a soloist or by a small group of three or four singers. The *Alleluia* and the refrain should be sung by the congregation accompanied by full choir.

59. YOU I CARRY, O LORD
Text:

Antiphon: Communion Prayer of the Maronite Liturgy. This antiphon speaks of an ancient manner of receiving communion which is being restored in the liturgical renewal. (See text of St. Cyril of Jerusalem, p. 24.)
Verse 1: *Jn. 6:51.*
Verse 2: *Jn. 6:36.*

Verse 3: Through Jesus, his Son, the Father reconciled to himself the universe whether on the earth or in the heavens, making peace through the blood of the cross. *Col. 1:20.*

Verse 4: *Mt. 27:34.*

Verse 5: *Mt. 27:29-30.*

Verse 6: Mt. *27:59-60.*

Verse 7: God the Father has redeemed us not according to our works, but according to his purpose and the grace which was granted to us in Christ Jesus. Our saviour Jesus Christ has destroyed death and brought to light life and immortality. *2 Tim. 1:9-10.*

Verse 8: The pilgrims of Emmaus said to the Lord, "Stay with us, for the evening is approaching and the day is now far spent." And he went in with them. And he sat at the table with them. He took bread, said the benediction, broke the bread, and began handing it to them. Then their eyes were opened and they recognized him. *Lk. 24:29-32.*

Verse 9: Lord, remember us when you come into your kingdom. And Jesus answered, "Amen, I say to you, this day you shall be with me in paradise." *Lk. 23:42-43.*
(Verses 3 to 7 are especially appropriate during the Lenten season).

Musical Performance:

Tempo, Antiphon — moderately. ♩• = 60. Verses — more slowly.

60. LONG LIVE THE LORD

Musical Performance:

Tempo, allegretto. ♩ = 72.

Each verse has three parts. The first and second are answered by the congregation with the words, "For he is my savior." Only the third part is answered by the antiphon, "Long live the Lord." Keeping in mind this basic framework of the psalm should make its performance easier.

61. THE SPIRIT OF GOD

Musical Performance:

Tempo, not too slowly.

In the performance of the verses, the words of the third line of music ("called to proclaim," etc.) should be emphasized. To accomplish this, the first and second lines may be sung by tenors and basses, the third by a soloist, the fourth by sopranos and altos.

62. ON THE DAY

Text:

Antiphon: inspired by the words of *2 Pet. 1:19.*
Verse 1: *1 Cor. 15:20* and *Ps. 63:2.*

Musical Performance:

Tempo, solemnly. ♩ = 60.

63. WITHOUT SEEING YOU

Text:

Antiphon: adapted from *1 Pet. 1:8.*

Verse 1: *Jn. 11:25-26.*

Verse 4: With Christ I am nailed to the cross. It is no longer I that live but Christ lives in me. And I live in the faith of the Son of God who loved me and gave himself up for me. *Gal. 2:20.*

Verse 8: Christ has died for his nation; and not only for his nation, but that he might gather into one the children of God who are scattered abroad. *Jn. 11:52.*

The words, "O Lord, to whom shall we go," are Peter's profession of faith to Christ in *Jn. 6:68.*

116

Musical Performance:

Tempo, not too slowly. $\quad = 72$.

In the performance we must distinguish three musical levels:

    1) congregation and choir for the antiphon;

    2) soloist (or 3 or 4 voices) for the first part of the verses;

    3) choir only for the second part of the verses ("O Lord, to whom . . .").

64. JESUS CHRIST, THE FAITHFUL WITNESS

Musical Performance:

Antiphon — solemnly. $\quad = 54$. Pay strict attention to the accidentals.

    Verses: The text is sung by a soloist or a small group of voices. The accompaniment can be provided by the organ alone, or by the choir humming, or by both. The dynamics must flow from the text of the verses. The soloist's primary concern should be textual interpretation rather than strict adherence to the notes.

65. WE GIVE YOU THANKS

Text:

The text comes from the Eastern liturgies which used it as an acclamation for the people during the Eucharistic Prayer. The original Greek Text for the opening words, "We give you thanks," is *eucharistoumen,* which also signifies "We make the Eucharist."

Verses 1 & 2: I am the bread of life; he who comes to me shall not hunger, and he who believes in me shall never thirst. *Jn. 6:35.*

Liturgical Use:

Communion Processional; Eucharist. The antiphon can also be used as an acclamation for the people during the Eucharistic Prayer, especially after the consecration of the bread and wine.

Musical Performance:

Tempo, not too slowly. $\quad = 72$.

In the second part of the verse, the sopranos and altos sing in unison. The rhythm should be maintained strictly.

66. BLESSED BE OUR LORD

Musical Performance:

Tempo, with joyful movement. $\quad = 92$.

The verses should be sung by a soloist or a small group of voices, the antiphon by the choir and congregation.

67. WHERE TWO OR THREE ARE GATHERED

Text:

Antiphon: *Mt. 18:20.*

    Verses: The verses speak of the different ways in which Christ is present in the congregation:

    He is present in the congregation itself gathered together in his name (verse 1).

    He is present in his word (verse 2).

    He is present in the Eucharist (verse 3).

Verse 4: adapted from *Jn. 11:52.*

The word "Emmanuel" has been used at the end of the verses because of its meaning, "God with us." *Is. 8:10* and *Rev. 21:3.*

Musical Performance:

Tempo, peacefully. $\quad = 72$.

The verses will sound better when sung in harmony by sopranos and altos rather than by tenors and basses because the range is comparatively low. The beginning ("Stay with us, Lord Jesus Christ") and the end ("O Lord, our God, Emmanuel") of the verses may be sung with the sopranos and tenors taking the higher notes in unison, and the altos and basses the lower notes in unison.

68. THIS IS THE DAY

Text:
Antiphon: *Ps. 118:24.*
The verses are inspired by a hymn from the liturgy of the early centuries of Christianity.

Musical Performance:
Tempo, allegretto. ♪ = 176.
The *alleluia* ending the verses can be sung alternately by sopranos and altos, and by tenors and basses.

69. GOD IS LOVE

Text:
Antiphon: *1 Jn. 4:16.*
Verse 2: Our eyes look hopefully to you, in due time;
        and you give us food.
        You open wide your hand, and
            grant the desires of all creatures. *Ps. 145:15.*
Verse 3: *1 Jn. 1:10.*
Verse 5: See how the Father loves us:
        we are called children of God;
        and such we are. *1 Jn. 3:1.*

Musical Performance:
Tempo, slowly and meditatively. ♩ = 60.
The beginning of the verses should be sung rather by sopranos and altos than by tenors and basses. The minor melody should be sung lightly and flowingly, without becoming dramatic.

70. AWAKE AND LIVE

Text:
Antiphon: *Eph. 5:14.*
Verse 1: *Rom. 6:3-4.*
Verse 2: *Jn. 4:14; 6:58.*
Verse 3: You were sealed with the Holy Spirit of the promise, who is the pledge of our inheritance, for the redemption of God's people for the praise of his glory. *Eph. 1:13-14.*
Verse 4: You have received the spirit of adoption as sons; by him we cry: "Abba! Father!" The Spirit himself gives testimony to our spirit that we are sons of God. *Rom. 8:15-16.*
Verse 5: *Rev. 21:1-4.*
Verse 7: You are a letter of Christ written not with ink but with the Holy Spirit of the living God, not on tablets of stone but on fleshly tablets of the heart. *2 Cor. 3:3.*

Liturgical Use:
Easter; Sundays; Baptism. Each verse of this hymn can be adapted to the various stages of the baptismal rite: the "Our Father," the profession of faith, the water, the light, and the white robe.

Musical Performance:
Tempo, not too slowly. ♩ = 72.

71. WHERE LOVE AND CHARITY ABIDE

Musical Performance:
Tempo, moderato. ♩ = 72.
The syncopation in the verses should no be accented, because the flow of the melody should be even.

72. YOU ALONE ARE HOLY

Text:
Antiphon: Following the "Apostolic Constitutions" of about 380, this text was sung at the mass at communion time.

Verse 1: *Jn. 1:1-18.*

Verse 2: *Lk. 4:16-22.*

Verse 3: I am the light cf the world, says the Lord. He who follows me does not walk in the darkness but will have the light of life. *Jn. 8:12.*

Verse 4: Come to me, all you who labor and are burdened, and I will give you rest.

(and 7) Take my yoke upon you and learn from me, for I am gentle and humble of heart and you will find rest for your souls. For my yoke is easy and my burden light. *Mt. 11:28-30.*

Verse 5: *Jn. 14:6; 2 Cor. 1:20; Col. 1:20; Jn. 1:29.*

Commentary:

In joy let us sing to Our Lord.

You alone are holy; you alone are Lord;

You alone are Jesus Christ.

Liturgical Use:

Feasts of Christ; Entrance Hymn; Communion.

Musical Performance:

♩ = 80.

The structure of the psalm is as follows:

    1. A: F minor "For you are God's son . . . "

       B: F major "Sing to the Lord . . . "

    2. A¹: F minor "You live . . . "

       B¹: F major "Sing to the Lord . . . "

The sopranos and the altos together may alternate with the tenors and the basses together in singing the various sections, such as: alternating voices between 1 AB and 2 A¹B¹, 1 A and 1 B, or 2A¹ and 2 B¹.

73. WITH WORDS OF PRAISE

Text:

Antiphon and Verse 1: adapted from *Ps 71:8,23.*

    Verse 2: *Lk. 2:32.*

Musical Performance:

♩ = 72.

The end of the antiphon, "Joy of my heart," should be sung more slowly and with greater intensity and solemnity than its beginning Take care that each verse begins with the words, "O my Lord." The first two lines of the verses can be sung either by soloists or by a small group of voices.

74. LORD, IN YOUR TENDERNESS

Text:

Antiphon and Verse 1: adapted from *Ps. 68:10-11.*

    Verse 2: *Jn. 6:35-39.*

    Verse 3, 4: *Jn. 10:14-16.*

    Verse 5, 6: *Ps. 68:4.*

Musical Performance:

♩ = 72.

For a well-balanced performance it is necessary to maintain a steady rhythm throughout the antiphon and the verses.

75. ALL PRAISE, GLORY, AND WISDOM

Musical Performance:

Antiphon — Largo. ♩ = 72.

The congregation should sing only the "Amen" in the antiphon. The seven terms of the doxology extol the majesty of God; therefore the music and the singing of the congregation must possess a glory expressive of that same majesty.

The small notes of the last "Amen" in the antiphon are sung by the congregation.

The verses are sung in recitative style. The accompaniment can be furnished by the organ, or by the choir, or by both.

76. YOU, LORD, ARE THE WAY

Text:

The text is built on the ten "I am" sentences, in which the Lord reveals himself and his mission.

Antiphon: I am the way, the truth and the life. *Jn. 14:6.*

    Verse 1: I am the light of the world.
           He who follows me
           will not walk in darkness,
           but will have the light of life. *Jn. 8:12.*

    Verse 2: I am the true vine;
           you are the branches. *Jn. 15:1,5.*

    Verse 3: *Jn. 4:14.*

    Verse 4: I am the bright morning star *Rev. 22:16.*

    Verse 6: I am the good shepherd. *Jn. 10:11.*

    Verse 7: I am the resurrection and the life. *Jn. 11:25.*

Musical Performance:

Antiphon — powerfully and joyfully. ♩ = 72.

The initial D-major section of the verses is sung by soloists or a small group of voices.

77. GIVE THE BREAD OF LIFE

Musical Performance:

Tempo, moderato. ♩ = 80.

The verses are constructed in the following manner:

    Section A: "God, my God . . ." in F minor.
      Refrain: "Your praise . . ." in F major.
             "And the joy of your love . . ." in F major.
    Section B: "My flesh is longing . . . " in F minor.

In order to emphasize this structure, sections A and B can, for instance, be sung by tenor and bass; the refrain "Your praise . . . , " by soprano and alto; and the refrain "And the joy . . . " in four-part harmony.

78. LET ME SING OF YOUR LAW

Musical Performance:

Tempo, Largo. ♩ = 72.

79. SALVATION, GLORY AND POWER

Musical Performance:

Antiphon: ♩. = 72. Verses can be slower: ♩. = 60.

The verses can be executed by an SATB choir only. The verse text is sung alternately by tenors and basses; the *alleluia*'s, by the remainder of the choir. The contrapuntal *alleluia* section should enhance rather than overpower the text.

80. JOY TO YOU

Text:

    Verse 1: *Lk. 1:26-27.*
    Verse 2: *Lk. 1:28, 38.*
    Verse 3: *Mt. 1:1, 16.*
    Verse 4: *Lk. 1:42, 48.*
    Verse 5: *Lk. 1:35; Jn. 1:14.*
    Verse 6: *Lk. 2:12-14.*
    Verse 7: *Lk. 2:15-19, 33.*
    Verse 8: *Mt. 2:11; Lk. 2:22-35.*
    Verse 9: *Is. 7:14; Soph. 3:14-17.*
    Verse 10: *Jn. 19:25-27; Acts 1:14.*
    Verse 11: *Rev. 12:1.*

Commentary:
> Mary, Mother of the Lord, said,
> "Behold, henceforth all generations
> shall call me blessed."
> Let us fulfill this prophecy of Our Lady
> by singing her glory,
> thus also praising her son.

Liturgical Use:
Feasts of Our Lady.

Musical Performance:
Tempo, with joyful movement. ♩ = 92.
The verses are best performed by a soloist or by a group of only three or four voices. The accompaniment can be executed by the organ, or by the choir humming, or by both.

81. WITHIN YOUR SPLENDOR

Text:
Antiphons: The texts of the antiphons are taken from the Roman liturgy, which used Psalm 45 for the first antiphon and the *Canticle of Canticles* for the second, applying the words to Our Lady. In these texts, Our Lady represents the beauty of the Church and is the bride of Jesus Christ.

Musical Performance:
First antiphon: ♩ = 72.
Second antiphon: ♩ = 60.

83. LORD, HAVE MERCY

Musical Performance:
Tempo, ♩ = 66.
The structure of this *Kyrie* and *Christe* is as follows:
> Soloist: "Lord, have mercy."
> Congregation: "Lord, have mercy."
> Choir: "Lord, have mercy."

The prayer of the soloist is repeated by the congregation; then the choir amplifies, by means of harmony, that same prayer of the congregation.

86. YOUR WORDS, O LORD

Text:
Verses: *Ps. 19:8-9.*

Liturgical Use:
This *alleluia* can be sung at the procession of the Gospel, when the lectionary is taken from the altar and carried to the ambo. Repeating its verses can make it last for the length of the procession.

Musical Performance:
Tempo, solemnly, but not too slowly. ♩ = 88.

87. GENERAL INTERCESSIONS

Liturgical Use:
This section proposes different responses which can be used after each intention of the General Intercessions (Prayer of the Faithful). The performance can follow the structure given below (using response 3 as an example):

Priest:	Introduction.
Soloist or choir:	REMEMBER US, O LORD.
Congregation and choir:	REMEMBER US, O LORD.
Commentator (or priest):	For . . . let us pray.
Congregation and choir:	REMEMBER US, O LORD.
Commentator (or priest):	For . . . let us pray.
Congregation and choir:	REMEMBER US, O LORD.
Commentator (or priest):	Let us pray also for our personal intentions. *(Silence)*
Priest:	Closing prayer.

It is wise to conclude each intention with a constant formula, which will invariably be a cue for the people's response. Such a formula could be "Let us pray" or "We pray to you, O Lord." However, do not use such a formula as "Let us pray" to elicit such a response as "We pray to you, O Lord." Rather employ another formula that does not have such a strong resemblance to the response itself, such as "We implore your love" or "We beseech you." For the Christmas season, the response "Glory to God on high" could be elicited by the formulas "We pray to you and sing your love" and "Let us sing and pray." The response, "Kyrie eleison," can be used in an ecumenical sense. These words, which we find in the Gospels, give witness to the presence of the Eastern Church in our worship.

Musical Performance:

The tempos must always be moderate, because the responses are to be sung by the entire congregation. A good prayer necessitates a good musical performance of the response, yet the music must always be kept subordinate to the essence of the prayer itself.

88. IF YOU BRING YOUR GIFT
Musical Performance:

Tempo, moderato. ♩ = 72.

89. WITH A JOYFUL HEART
Musical Performance:

The tempo for the antiphon and verses should be moderate. ♩ = 79.

The verses can be sung by a small group until the entire congregation knows the melody by memory. Take care not to rush the first three notes of the next to last measure.

90. HOLY, HOLY, HOLY
Musical Performance:

Tempo, moderato. ♩ = 80.

Suggestions for the *Hosanna:* The choir can sing the antiphon in unison, repeating it with full harmony accompanied by the congregation. The *Hosanna* is repeated after each verse. The rhythm should be maintained strictly throughout; if, after the completion of a a verse, a beat of rest is needed before he repetition of the *Hosanna*, it should be in keeping with the established rhythm, so that the *Hosanna* comes in on a definite beat.

91. ACCLAMATIONS
Liturgical Use:

These acclamations can be used in the Eucharistic Prayer to promote greater congregational participation in the presidential prayer of the priest. They are to be sung after the consecration of the bread (when the priest shows the host) and after the consecration of the wine (when he shows the chalice). Acclamations can also be sung three or four times during special masses after the individual parts of the Eucharistic Prayer, thus adding solemnity. The priest can introduce the congregational singing of the acclamation with the the words, "We sing to you, Lord."

Musical Performance:

Tempo, moderato, keeping the rhythm strictly. ♩ = 72.

92. CHRIST HAS DIED
Musical Performance:

Tempo, with great solemnity. ♩ = 60.

93. THE GREAT AMEN
Liturgical Use:

The triple *Amen* emphasizes the acclamation of the people at the end of the Eucharistic Prayer. But the answer of the people must be evoked by the priest. Therefore the words "Through him . . ." must be proclaimed in a festive way, and the ending words "Forever and ever" should be sung on one note in order to give the people their note for beginning. This system, called *ekphonesis*, is used in other liturgies. If this method is not used, it is impossible for the people to begin their *Amen* correctly.

Musical Performance:
A slow, dignified tempo.

96. LAMB OF GOD

Musical Performance:
The structure of this litany is as follows:
Choir: "Lamb of God,
you take away the sins of the world,
have mercy on us."
Congregation and Choir: "Have mercy on us."
The performance is not difficult, although it may appear complicated. Indeed, each "Lamb of God" has the same melody and harmony as the preceding one but is sung two notes higher. In the part sung by the choir, the tenor and bass parts have the role of accompaniment, repeating "Lamb of God" as an unending supplication. Their accompaniment must be light, supporting the soprano and alto rather than subduing them.

97. IN THE PEACE OF CHRIST

Text:
The verses proclaim the meaining of the mass:
Verse 1 — the celebration of the Word of God;
Verse 2 — the celebration of the Eucharist;
Verse 3 — the joy and the duty of bringing each of the aforementioned two parts of the mass to the rest of the world.

Musical Performance:
Tempo, in a joyful manner; not too slowly. ♩ = 72.

INDEX for VOLUME II

(Title and first line of hymn)

Index for Volume II (cont.)

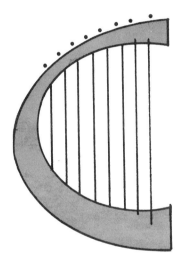